D1096345

The Cat ENCYCLOPEDIA

ANIWA PUBLISHING

ROYAL CANIN

Contributors

SCIENTIFIC ADVISORS

PROFESSOR BERNARD-MARIE PARAGON,
National Veterinary School of Alfort,
President, French Society of Feline Science

JEAN-PIERRE VAISSAIRE,
Doctor of Veterinary Medicine

And in alphabetical order:

Bacqué	Hélène	UMES – National Veterinary School of Alfort
Beugnet	Frédéric	Lecturer – National Veterinary School of Alfort
Biourge	Vincent	D.V.M. – Royal Canin Research Center
Blanchard	Géraldine	D.V.M. – National Veterinary School of Alfort
Bossé	Philippe	Professor – National Veterinary School of Alfort
Bullard-Cordeau	Brigitte	Editor-in-chief – Animal Junior
Casteran	Martine	Editor-in-chief – Atout Chat
Chatelain	Éliane	Professor – National Veterinary School of Lyon
Chaurand	Jean-Paul	D.V.M. – National Veterinary School of Alfort
Crépin	Fabrice	D.V.M. – Royal Canin
Déboise	Mikael	Researcher – Royal Canin Research Center
Fortamps	Béatrice	Editorial Coordinator – Diffomédia
Fradin-Ferme	Michèle	D.V.M. – Clinical Practitioner
Gagnon	Anne-Claire	D.V.M. – Vice President, French Society of Feline Science
Ganivet	Alain	D.V.M. – Clinical Practitioner
Garcia	Catherine	Training Director, Feline Science – Royal Canin
Gogny	Marc	Professor – National Veterinary School of Nantes
Grandjean	Dominique	Lecturer – National Veterinary School of Alfort
Guillot	Jacques	Lecturer – National Veterinary School of Alfort
Hugues	François	D.V.M. – Journalist, Europe 1
Kretz	Catherine	D.V.M. – Secretary, French Society of Feline Science
Lagarde	Henri	Chief Executive Officer – Royal Canin
Levesque	Anne	Research Center – Royal Canin
Moraillon	Anne	D.V.M. – National Veterinary School of Alfort
Morris	James G.	Professor – University of California, Davis
Pibot	Pascale	D.V.M. – Royal Canin Research Center
Pierson	Philippe	D.V.M. – Royal Canin
Samaille	Jean-Pierre	D.V.M. – Journalist, L'Action Vétérinaire
Soriano	Bruno	Journalist – Chat magazine
Vaissaire	Josée	D.V.M. – Member, Veterinary Academy of France

Publishing Managment
BERNARDO GALLITELLI,
Chief Executive Officer
Aniwa S.A.

GUY ROLLAND
Aniwa Publishing

"The smallest feline is a masterpiece."

LEONARDO DA VINCI

An Invitation to the World of the Cat

The cat, master of the house, so close yet so distant, so familiar yet so mysterious, has always fascinated humans with its looks and behavior.

Long-time inhabitants of the desert and savanna, cats still carry their biological needs and character within, as part of their physiology. Their character, like that of their distant ancestors, is a subtle combination of nonchalance and adventurousness.

From the deserts of yore to the countryside and cities of today, the feline world has changed rapidly:

- in thirty years, the number of feline breeds resulting from planned hybridization conducted by humans has virtually tripled, from some twenty in 1960 to over fifty at the end of the century.
- spectacular scientific knowledge has been acquired recently.

A specialist in premium feline nutrition, Royal Canin has long followed the tracks of this ancient solitary hunter. Major scientific advances of the past few years have brought us beyond the two traditional roles of nutrition (to build and maintain the organism, and to provide energy) and added a third: prevention. The notion of feline nutrition for health has been born.

Because humans domesticated cats, our primary task is to respect cats as animals, to feed them, and to ensure their health and well-being in accordance with their true specific needs, rather than based on our own human projections.
This is the approach of Royal Canin, a manufacturer specializing in premium feline nutrition which has always followed this ethic of true respect for the animal.

We hope this encyclopedia will help you discover a fascinating world rich with a long history and enhanced by the most recent scientific findings.

Thank you to all who contributed to creating this work: researchers at veterinary schools in France and abroad, as well as at the Royal Canin Research Center, under the direction of Professor Paragon and Dr. Vaissaire.

I invite you to explore these pages brimming with images and information and let yourself be swept away by the magical world of the cat, an intermingling of science and fantasy the cat offers us without restraint.

Henri LAGARDE,
Chief Executive Officer
Groupe Royal Canin

Foreword

Cats are not small dogs! Shameless hunters, cats have retained their original characteristics as strict carnivores from their hunting days. This explains why many of us are drawn to this exceptional companion and requires a careful respect for the cat's specific features, which each owner must know. This book is intended to reveal the big and small secrets that make up the cat.

The cohabitation of humans and cats, though it long remained distant, reaches back into the mists of time. The hunting skill of these small felines made them the natural protectors of granaries and kitchens. For this they were truly venerated in ancient Egypt. However, the cat's independence - sometimes bordering on disrespect - and the pagan practices with which cats were associated in the Middle Ages tarnished their image for a long time. Not until the literary salons of the 19th century and the world of artists did the cat come back into fashion. But this comeback was often at the price of the castration of males, a practice considered a means of re-entering the intelligentsia and acquiring a sort of perfection.

In our urban world, domestic cats carry a bit of the magic of the big cats, in their supple back, noble gait, and luminous gaze. We enjoy this and would hate to lose this pleasure. In France, one of every four households has at least one cat. Over eight million little felines will move in with us in the 21st century and, although most of this population might be considered "mixed breed cats," the fascination continues.

Yet another book on cats . . . but a book in which we aimed to combine knowledge, culture, and beauty; a book for an animal food manufacturer with contributions by scientists, writers, breeders, and enlightened cat fanciers. Because scientists are qualified to satisfy the natural curiosity of cat owners, we chose the best scientists for this project so that the basic knowledge gathered up to now could be made accessible to all in simple, precise terms. Because cats have been omnipresent in the world of humans throughout history, we sought proof of this presence in all forms of art and media. Because cats and beauty are closely intertwined, we aimed to gather the most beautiful illustrations in this book.

Sincere thanks to all who contributed to the technical, scientific, and aesthetic success of this work, particularly to my colleagues from the French Society of Feline Science. Our best reward will be the pleasure you find in exploring these pages and extracting the information that will help you better understand—and better love—your feline companion.

Professor B.-M. PARAGON,
President, French Society of Feline Science

Preface

Over eight million cats currently live in France. In the past decade, we made significant strides in our knowledge of this companion. For this reason, the project of making all the basic facts about this species accessible to the public, in an educational manner, is especially welcome.

By studying the origins and evolution of domestic cats, we can situate them within the Felids, of which the original type was the wild cat (Felis silvestris) that inhabited the large, Old World forests. Our Felis catus, represented by the many breeds described in the Cat Encyclopedia, is thought to have originated in Egypt from a wild felid living in Libya or eastern Africa.

Egyptian civilization gave the cat a privileged place among the gods. Bastet, the cat goddess of music, dance, and motherhood, appeared in the twenty-second dynasty, during the golden age of Pharaonic civilization.

Today, there are still many cat worshippers. Cat fanciers gather together in associations to work for the greater glory of the cat, although not always in perfect harmony. The merit of the Cat Encyclopedia is that it sums up the growing diversity of breeds and the ever-changing world of cat fancy.

Brought to France in the Middle Ages, the cat has remained highly present in art and the media. The appearance of cats in both pictorial works of the classical period and in works of animal artists of the 19th and 20th centuries shows that artists used these subjects to convey their anguish, joy, and fantasies.

The chapters covering the various aspects of daily life with a cat are of great practical value to the reader. Feline physiology and pathology are now much better understood, thanks to original work demonstrating that, contrary to an opinion long considered dogma, cats cannot be put in the same category as dogs. Cats have different nutritional needs, very different behavior, and, quite often, specific illnesses.

The Cat Encyclopedia, under the talented direction of Professor Bernard-Marie Paragon, brings together contributors who are the authority in their respective fields. They made often complex notions accessible to the general public. There is no doubt that cat lovers—I hesitate to write "owners," so true is it that, while you can own a dog, you instead live in your cat's home, with the cat always retaining a certain degree of independence—will find in this work the information they seek on their favorite animal.

Professor Robert MORAILLON,
Director, National Veterinary School of Alfort

Summary

True
respect
of the
Cat

As forgivable as it may be, treating the cat as if it were a little human being is a biological mistake that may prove to be dangerous for the animal.

Respecting the cat for what it gives us and represents to us should not consist of developing an anthropomorphic approach aiming to make the cat, as we often hear, "a child, if only it could speak". Biology is such that it preferred the earthly diversity of living creatures, making each one of them the complement of the others so as to tend towards a delicate balance that Man may not alter in any way.

This anthropomorphic reflex, as forgivable as it may be, given the sometimes powerful emotions that we all feel towards our cats, must therefore be shunned as being disrespectful of their biological and physiological functioning and, consequently, may prove to be dangerous to them.

The best examples of this reality may be found in the daily diet

• Man can change his diet at each mealtime without problems ... but, if his digestive system were designed like that of the cat, such continuous dietary variation would give him constant problems with diarrhoea.

• Man needs cooked food, salt, sugar, appetizing smells and presentation of the food on his plate in order to enjoy his meal, but, if his senses were those of the cat, he would need only the merest hint of the latter to appreciate it completely ...

• For thousands of years, man has been able to take his time to eat his meals, without the risk of becoming the prey of a wild predator but, if he were a cat, evolution would have left him with more of that reflex of rapid consumption imprinted in the genes of all animals likely to have their food stolen by a member of its own species or be attacked by a predator ...

• Man takes his meals at regular intervals (morning, midday, evening), but the cat is originally a lone hunter of desert lands who provides for his dietary needs by a succession of small meals, morning, noon and night (up to 16 a day).

So, with all due deference; cats are cats. They must be appreciated, treated and respected as such. And, if we consider the examples already mentioned, science and observation will only support these facts.

The digestion is a typical example of the reactions and mechanisms proper to each species, any assimilation may prove to be dangerous for the cat (or for humans), the differences being so obvious and the behaviour patterns so dissimilar.

The passage of food in the organism allows a better understanding of these key notions.

Generally speaking, the human digestive system represents 11% of the body weight, compared with only 2.8% to 3.5% for the cat. Hardly surprising to hear that Man is better able to digest the most varied elements.

Food appreciation: smell and taste differently involved

The cat, unlike human beings, appreciates its food first and foremost by smell. The surface of its nasal mucus is 10 times greater than that of humans. A cat's nose contains up to 67 million olfactory receptors, while the most sensitive human nose has no more than 20 million. Taste, however, despite the received wisdom, is only very marginally involved in the cat's food preferences. While humans have some 9 000 "taste buds" (the cells that receive and analyse the taste of food), the cat has 19 times fewer and, once in its mouth, the food does not linger on the tongue but is sent very quickly towards the stomach. The cat, which does not respond particularly to sweet tastes, is a strict carnivore that does not "synthetise" taurine, but finds it exclusively in the flesh of the animals it hunts or in prepared croquettes.

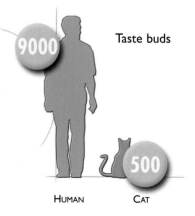

Taste buds

9000

500

HUMAN   CAT

Predigestion: *from the oral cavity to the stomach*

The cat spends very little of its time chewing its food. It eats hastily, whereas humans ready their food for digestion by prolonged chewing, finding pleasure by releasing flavours and, by grinding the food down and mixing it with saliva, and begins the first stage of digestion via the enzymes contained in the latter. For the cat, however, the stomach is the chief location where the processes of digestion are started.

Scientific reality shows us once again: the stomach represents more than 60% of the total weight of the digestive system of the feline species compared with only 11% for humans.
The very acid stomach pH, plus the large amounts of hydrochloric acid (6 times greater than in humans), equips the cat's stomach admirably for its function as a purifier, providing it with an extraordinarily efficient natural barrier against digestive infections.

Weight of digestive tract as percentage of body weight	11%	2,8% to 3,5%
Surface of nasal mucus	2 à 3 cm^2	20 cm^2
Olfactory cells	5 to 20 million	60 to 65 million
Taste buds	9 000 buds	500 buds
Dentition	32 teeth	30 teeth
Mastication	prolonged	no chewing
Salivary digestive enzymes	YES	NO
Duration of food intake	1 hour	multiple meals
Stomach capacity	1,3 l	0,3 l
Stomach pH	2 to 4	1 to 2
Length of small intestine	6 to 6,5 m	1 to 1,7 m
Length of large intestine	1,5 m	0,3 to 0,4 m
Density of intestinal flora	10 000 000 bacteria/g	10 000 bacteria/g
Duration of intestinal transit	30 hours to 5 days	12 to 24 hours
Adult glucid requirement	60 to 65% of the dry matter	low
Adult protein requirement	8 to 12% of the dry matter	25 to 40% of the dry matter
Adult lipid requirement	25 to 30% of the dry matter	15 to 45% of the dry matter
Dietary habit	**omnivore**	**carnivore**

Digestive performance: *inherited in the genes*

Originally, the cat is a "nibbler". In fact, if food is left out for it, the cat will make between 10 and 16 snacks a day. The cat also drinks about 10 times a day. Meals last only 2 to 3 minutes. These small quantities spread throughout the day explain why the digestive transit is very rapid in the cat compared with that of humans (12 to 24 hours compared with 30 to 48 hours).

To understand these elements, which may also be considered in other biological functional aspects, is to understand the cat, and above all to accept that the cat is very different to the human, not only in its appearance or in the fact that it cannot "speak". The sometimes-extreme anthropomorphism touted in certain films, for instance, is not only scientifically regrettable, but is actually very harmful and may even reduce the life expectancy of the animal.

The differences between man and cat

*Physiological differences
and differences in basic dietary habit mean
that each has specific nutritional needs.*

Failure to recognize the real needs of the animal, combined with every owner's natural desire to "do the best", may represent a danger to our animals by projecting on to them our wishes, our lifestyles, without taking account of the essential: their animal nature.

Responsible for the domestication of the cat, man has the duty of feeding it according to its true specific needs, and not according to any human projections. The animal is an animal, and in no way a human being as regards its biology. This is the first rule of true respect of the animal. The choice of food best adapted to one's animal must therefore be guided by a dietary approach that is not influenced by one's own eating habits.

Since the dawn of time Man has been an omnivore, blessed with a sense of taste and enjoying variety to dispel boredom, whereas the organism of the cat, a strict carnivore, is adapted to one particular type of food. Although it is sometimes tempting to

apply the rule of diversity to your cat and serve it food more closely resembling a human meal, this would be ill-adapted to its condition or its morphology. Nearly 5 000 years of domestication of the feline race have not succeeded in transforming these strict carnivores into omnivores.

The same applies to all those little pleasures we offer them in the image of those we treat ourselves to. Butter, a spoonful of yoghurt, fish, cheese, ... all these little "extras" disturb the perfectly balanced ration calculated by a nutritionist. Such imbalances may result in intestinal problems and slowly but surely debilitate the animal. We must remain on our guard and curb our anthropomorphic instincts that may harm the good health of our animals.

From "feeding" to "Health Nutrition"

*To enjoy life
as long as possible*

Although death is, and will remain, an inescapable biological process, it is also true that immense progress has been made in medical science, especially on the preventive side of the equation, now ensuring our feline friends a steadily increasing life expectancy.

An extraordinary improvement in nutrition:

In the past 30 years, the foods prepared by animal feed manufacturers for domestic pets have brought about a revolutionary change in the conditions of life of our cats, formerly fed on scraps and leftovers. It has been estimated that cats have acquired nearly 5 years of additional life expectancy in the past 15 years alone.

It is quite probable that the years to come will bring even higher figures, since three major advances have been made in the past 30 years:

• until 1980, a cat was simply "fed" to stop it feeling hungry,

• after 1980, Health Nutrition took its first steps by allowing for 2 parameters: the Age of the animal and its Level of Activity,

• 1997 to 2000 marks the arrival of Health Nutrition with two new dimensions: Prevention and type of Breed. Four parameters were now taken into account: not only Age and Activity, but also Breed and Physiological Condition of the animal.

The four objectives of health nutrition

1 - To build up/sustain the organism
2 - To provide energy
3 - To nourish and to prevent
4 - To nourish and to treat

It is now possible to formulate feeds in the light of clearly identified requirements, according to known and indexed deficiencies that have to be combated, and to specificities discovered along the way as research moves onwards. Scientists now realise that cats do not have to be fed the same way regardless of whether they are kittens, adults, elderly, pregnant or neutered … all of which are elements to take into account in their daily diet.

This realisation is growing daily and allows the development of the simple Feed (feeding to sustain the animal), and the Basic Nutrition (meeting the nutritional needs of the organism), then going on to Health Nutrition, where a distinction is made between two complementary approaches: "Nourish and Prevent" and "Nourish and Treat".

So, driven by scientific research in veterinary medicine, the traditional concept of nutrition, namely building up/sustaining the organism and providing energy, has transformed in a matter of years to include the dimensions of prevention and, under certain conditions, treatment.

Basic Nutrition (Nutritional Needs of the Organism)

1 - Building up/sustaining the organism:
Amino acids, minerals, trace elements, vitamins, proteins and certain lipids meet the minimum nutritional need to build up and sustain the organism.

▶ **Growth, reproduction, muscles, coat...:** proteins
Nervous system, skeleton, teeth, blood...: minerals and trace elements
Sight, reproduction, skeleton, cells ...: vitamins
Cell membranes: lipids

2 - Providing energy:
Lipids, carbohydrates and, to a lesser extent, proteins give the animal the necessary energy.

▶ **Energy, appetite:** lipids
Energy, digestion: carbohydrates
Non-essential amino acids

Health Nutrition

Nutrition is now - and this is at least one point of convergence between man and catkind - a key aspect of prevention, probably even the most important; this accounts for its being considered as the first among medicines (as did Hippocrates in antiquity) … and no doubt the gentlest of them all.

3 - Nourish and prevent:
Certain nutrients are integrated in the prevention of risks such as kidney diseases, digestive problems or the effects of old age …

▶ **Bone condition:** calcium, excess fatty deposits
Kidney problems: reduced phosphorus levels
Digestive problems: addition of "prebiotics", fermentable fibres encouraging good balance of the intestinal flora, proteins
Premature ageing: vitamins E-C, essential fatty acids, grape and green-tea polyphenols

4 - Nourish and treat:
To aid recovery from certain illnesses, highly specific nutrients will be included in or left out of the food as part of the therapeutic and convalescent processes.

▶ **Kidneys, allergies, heart, obesity, intestines**

"Nutrients" approach
and "Ingredients" approach

The **"Nutrients"** *approach:*
a **"nutritional jigsaw puzzle"**
with fifty pieces.

This presentation of the concept of nutrition in general and health nutrition in particular thus reinforces the distinction between two approaches with regard to the formulation of products for use in animal feeding: the "Nutrients" approach and the "Ingredients" approach.

The **"Nutrients" approach** allows the formulation of a balanced feed by the putting together of a veritable "jigsaw puzzle" of some fifty "nutrients". Each one of them is indispensable for the health of the animal. In the right proportions, the nutrients represent a more of less large part of each piece of the puzzle. This composition makes possible the accomplishment of the four main objectives of Health Nutrition (building up and sustaining the organism,

providing energy, nourishing and preventing, nourishing and treating), taking account of the parameters of Age, Level of Activity, Breed and Physiological Condition. It also meets the real precise and specific needs of each animal.

The **"Ingredients" approach**, on the other hand, is no more than a simple list of standardised elements (or primary alimentary materials if you will) used in the composition of a food preparation, sometimes even with a simple anthropomorphic vision, as if the animal had the palate and the digestive system of a human. It therefore proves to be less precise, and above all disregards the real needs of the animal.

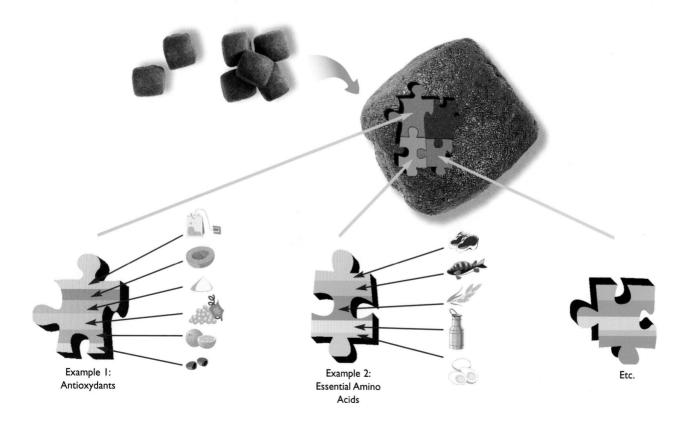

Example 1:
Antioxydants

Example 2:
Essential Amino
Acids

Etc.

Nutrients or ingredients?
The "Ingredients" trap

25% fresh meat ▬▬ = ▬▬ 4 à 5% de proteins

How does a feed containing 25% of fresh meat in fact contribute only 4% to 5% of the proteins originating in the fresh meat?

Nourishing a cat properly is therefore a 2-stage operation:

1st stage: a genuine understanding of the animal, its physiology, its biology, its behaviour and, therefore, the real needs of its organism.

2nd stage: an equally scientific approach not only to the nutrients intended to cover these needs, but also to those intended to generate the preventive side - or, as the case may be, the curative side - of the prepared animal feed.

A genuinely nutritional feed is therefore most often a veritable jigsaw puzzle of 50 or 60 essential nutrients (proteins, minerals, vitamins, trace elements, lipids, carbohydrates, …), whereas the seduction of an eye-catching list of "Ingredients" is only very anthropomorphic and serves no real purpose beyond that of flattering the master ("chicken flavour", "lamb", "salmon").

As surprising as it may seem, the protein content of a feed claiming "25% fresh meat" is only between 4% and 5% of the total weight on the dry matter. In fact, the regulations require the pet food manufacturers to list the ingredients by descending order of weight, before cooking. Fresh meat or certain ingredients containing large amounts of water may therefore be placed at the top of the list, creating the illusion of their being the main source of nutrition.

In the case of a feed claiming to contain 25% lamb, the dry croquette will therefore contain only 4% to 5% of lamb proteins after cooking. Suppose this feed also contains 20% maize, 20% rice, 15% dried fish, 10% poultry fat and 10% vegetable oil. The manufacturer can write "Lamb" in large characters as the main ingredient but, in reality, there is only 4% to 5% lamb proteins, while the cereals are the main ingredients in the finished feed in terms of quantity.

One feed, three different descriptions!

"with beef"	minimum 4% of beef
"with lamb"	minimum 4% of lamb
"with chicken"	minimum 4% of chicken
"rich in beef"	minimum 14% of beef
"rich in lamb"	minimum 14% of lamb

 Dry cat food "with beef" 4% beef

 Dry cat food "with lamb" 4% lamb

 Dry cat food "with chicken" 4% chicken

The same ingredients... the same foodstuffs... but 3 different names and 3 different packs

Another example: the same feed containing, among other ingredients, 4% chicken, 4% lamb and 4% beef may be labelled under three different descriptions: "chicken", "lamb" or "beef". And there will always be someone there to tell you that his animal prefers the lamb version, despite the fact that the actual lamb content is exactly the same as that of the chicken version.

However, this "Ingredients" approach, which has deceived more than one owner, fails to take account of the dosage, quantity, or quality, and of the variety of origins of nutrients - essential to life and adapted to the specific needs of cats - that ensure the quality of a balanced feed. A "standard" feed may, for instance, contain some fifteen nutrients, whereas a "pedigree" or "nutritional" feed will usually contain up to fifty.

Royal Canin, undisputed precursor of feline health nutrition

*Royal Canin: a nutrition concept
that wins the day by uncompromising
fidelity to its roots: "Knowledge and Respect".*

Since its creation, the veterinarians and nutritional experts at Royal Canin have directed their constant efforts towards achieving major advances in terms of canine and feline nutrition. Each year brings its crop of new nutritional programmes and new nutritional formulas that, besides the nutrients essential for maintaining healthy life, also incorporate natural elements to prevent certain diseases and to protect the animal.

1997
First world launch: a new generation of nutritional cat food products (RCFI range), targeted according to the age and physiological condition of the cat (Kitten, Fit , Sensible, Slim, Senior). This new generation resolutely abandoned the traditional anthropomorphic approach based on ingredients ("salmon", "chicken", …). The RCFI range was an immediate spectacular world-wide success.

1998
First feed developed specifically for castrated males and spayed females at veterinary clinics: Vet Cat, to Nourish and Prevent.

1999
Persian 30: result of the co-operation between R&D and the breeders, the first feed adapted to the physiognomy and the specific nutritional needs of Persian cats:
- development of the Almond 11 croquette,
- Derm system (for a healthy coat and skin care),
- Hairball Transit System (to help eliminate hairballs in the stomach).

2001
World launch of Indoor 27 ®, 1ˢᵗ feed formulated for indoor cats (hairballs, obesity, smell).

2001
V-Diet, to Nourish and Treat, the development of 6 dietary products for cats in particular:
- the hydrolysate for the Hypoallergenic Program,
- the hyperprotein diet for the Obesity Program.

2002
Launch of 4 big world firsts with the new Feline Nutrition range with cats in mind:
- Reinforcement of natural defences (Immunity Program),
- Campaign against cellular ageing (Anti-ageing Complex),
- Regeneration of coat and skin,
- Specially textured croquettes.

2002
Vet Cat Neutered: the first-ever nutritional super-prevention range to cater for the physiological specificities of cats, spayed females and castrated males.

Familiarity breeds respect

To define its products, Royal Canin does not conduct market research or consumer polls, but places the cat, its "one true client", at the centre of operations.
Knowledge of the real nutritional needs of the cat is derived from the daily experience of the partner breeders and the veterinary nutritionists and from the first-hand scientific observations of the Royal Canin Research and Development experts.

An original method allows Royal Canin, more than any other Brand, to be genuinely in the vanguard of innovation and nutritional precision.
A philosophy also based on the sharing of knowledge of the cat through reference works, such as guides to breeding and training and, of course, this Encyclopaedia of the Cat.

ROYAL CANIN

KNOWLEDGE AND RESPECT

THE BREEDS

VOLUME 1

Abyssinian   Maine Coon
Americain Bobtail   Persian
American Curl   Siamese

VOLUME 2

American Shorthair   Burmese
American Wirehair   Burmilla
Turkish Angora   California Spangled
Balinese   Ceylon
Bengal   Chartreux
Russian Blue   Norwegian Forest Cat
Bombay   Cornish Rex
British Shorthair

VOLUME 3

Cymric   Javanese
Devon Rex   Korat
European Shorthair   La Perm
Exotic Shorthair   Domestic Lynx
German Rex   Oriental Longhair
Havana   Manx
Japanese Bobtail

VOLUME 4

Egyptian Mau   Singapura
Munchk   Snowshoe
Ocicat   African Shorthair
Ojos Azules   Somali
Oriental Shorthair   Sphynx
Ragdoll   Tonkinese
Birman   Turkish Van
Scottisch Fold   York Chocolate
Selkirk Rex   Pixie Bob
Siberian Cat

Cymric

A longhaired, tailless cat from Ireland

A specific gene was responsible for the semilong coat of the cats living on the Isle of Man in the Irish Sea.

In the 1960s, Canadian breeder Blair Wright and American breeder Leslie Falteisek decided to fix this characteristic and thus created a new longhaired Manx breed, the Cymric (Cymru means Wales in Gaelic).

Around 1970, the Canadian Cat Association recognized the breed. Naming it Longhaired Manx, the C.F.A. recognized the breed in 1989. As of this writing, the F.I.Fe has not recognized the Cymric. This breed is almost unknown in Europe.

RED TABBY CYMRIC. ORIGINATING ON THE ISLE OF MAN, THE CYMRIC (KIM RICK) WAS SELECTIVELY BRED IN THE UNITED STATES WHERE IT WAS ALSO REFERRED TO AS LONGHAIRED MANX.

13

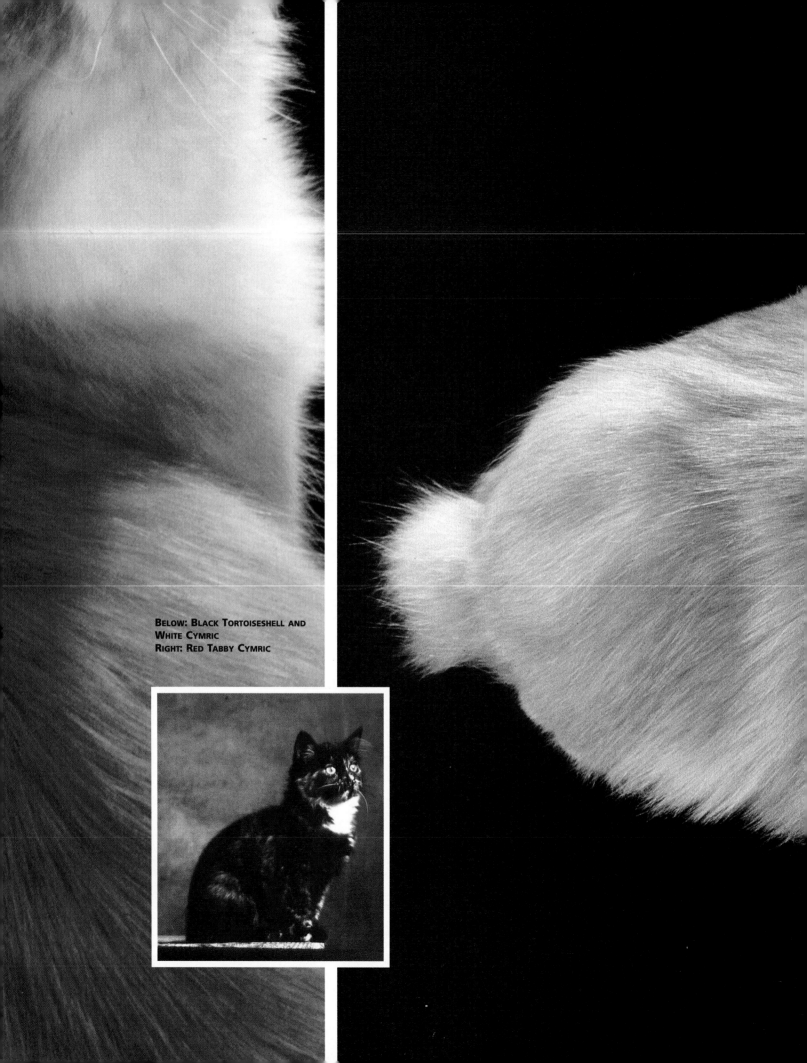

**BELOW: BLACK TORTOISESHELL AND
WHITE CYMRIC
RIGHT: RED TABBY CYMRIC**

Cymric

GENERAL
Manxlike. Weight: 3.5 to 5.5 kg.
Semilong to long coat.

BLACK TORTOISESHELL CYMRIC

HEAD
Of medium size, round and slightly longer than broad. Moderately rounded forehead, pronounced cheekbones, and jowliness. Nose of medium length. Muzzle slightly longer than broad. Definite whisker break. Strong chin.

EARS
Wide at the base with rounded tips. Set well apart.
Full interior furnishings.

EYES
Large and round. Color appropriate to coat color.

NECK
Short and thick.

BODY
Compact and cobby. Broad chest. Short back. Rounded rump. Robust bone structure. Solidly muscled.

LEGS AND PAWS
Hind legs are much longer than forelegs. Heavily boned. Muscular. Paws round and medium in size.

TAIL
Short or absent.

COAT
Semilong, longer on underparts. Very silky texture. Double coat (abundant undercoat). Colors: Same varieties as the Manx (natural colors, tabby patterns, etc.).

RED TABBY CYMRIC

WHITE TORTOISESHELL CYMRIC

RED TABBY AND WHITE CYMRIC

CHARACTERISTICS
This is a playful, active, hardy cat. The highly social Cymric readily acceptes strangers and gets along well with other animals. It is also gentle with children.
Care is simple. Weekly brushing is sufficient.

(▼)F.I.Fe (■) L.O.O.F. (★) C.F.A. (◆) T.I.C.A.

Devon Rex

Country of Origin: Great Britain
Other Name: Poodle Cat

A funny little creature with a lambswool coat and bat ears

In 1960 in Devon, England, Ms. Beryl Cox found a curly-coated male cat in a litter of feral cats living in an abandoned mine. This male was bred with a tricolor female, who gave birth to a curly-coated male that Ms. Cox named Kirlee. Kirlee was then bred with Cornish Rex cats. The resulting kittens had very straight hair, indicating that the two genes responsible for these two mutations, that of the Devon Rex and that of the Cornish Rex, were different and recessive. In an effort to pin down the mutant Devon Rex gene, Kirlee was extensively inbred. Unfortunately, this led to the appearance, in some lines, of a fatal hereditary disease known as "spasticity." But the breed has been closely monitored, and American and French breeders have worked together to breed healthy individuals with carefully planned pedigrees.

The Devon Rex was officially recognized by the F.I.Fe. in 1967.

In the United States, the breed was not distinguished from the Cornish Rex until after 1979. It is recognized by the C.F.A. and by T.I.C.A., which published a standard in 1988.

BROWN TABBY AND WHITE DEVON REX

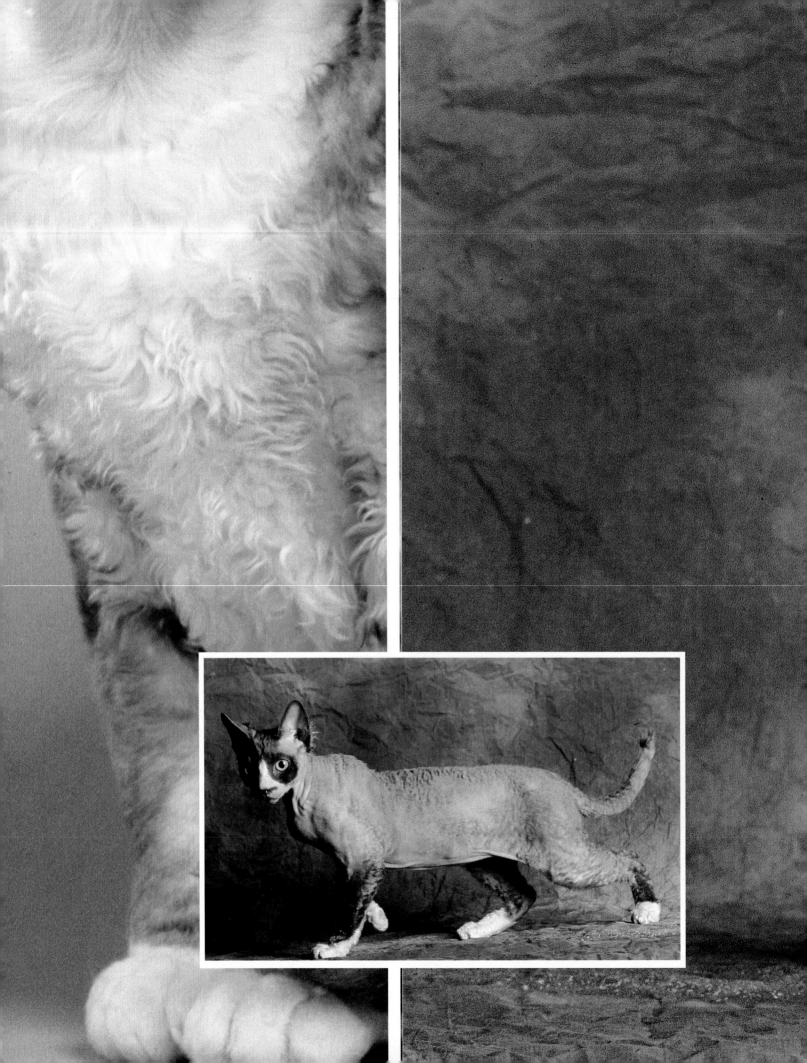

Devon Rex

GENERAL
Medium sized. Medium-limbed type.
Weight: 2.5 to 4 kg.
Very large ears.
Short, curly hair.

BLACK SMOKE DEVON REX

WHITE DEVON REX

TABBY AND WHITE CHOCOLATE DEVON REX

HEAD
Fairly small, wedge-shaped, short, angular. Flat skull, domed forehead. Full cheeks, prominent cheekbones. Short muzzle. Short nose. Well-marked stop (◆). Large chin. Well-marked whisker pinch. Curly, fairly harsh whiskers and eyebrows of medium length (▼).

EARS
Very large, very broad at the base, cone-shaped with rounded tips. Set very low, covered with fine hair. Sparse hair on the inside. Hairs on the ear tips (lynx tips).

EYES
Large, oval, well-spaced, set at an angle toward the outer edge of the ear. Luminous, clear, pure color corresponding to that of the coat.

NECK
Moderately long, thin, slightly arched.

BODY
Medium in size and length. Broad chest. Firm, strong muscles.

LEGS
Long, thin. Hind legs clearly longer than forelegs. Fine- to medium-boned. Muscular. Small, oval paws.

TAIL
Long, slender, tapering, well-furnished with short hair.

COAT
Short, fine, kinked, wavy hair with or without guard hairs. Coat not as neat as that of the Cornish Rex, but slightly wild like that of a Poodle or sheep. Some Devon Rexes have only down on the belly (▼).

As in the Cornish Rex, the hair grows slowly. All colors and patterns are allowed, with or without black.

NOTES
Allowable outcross breeds: none.

FAULTS
Narrow head like that of the Oriental Shorthair or broad head like that of the British Shorthair. Small, high-set eyes. Small eyes.

Stocky body. Short, hairless or shaggy tail. Close-lying coat. Wiry or smooth hair. Large, hairless areas.

DEVON REX KITTEN

BLUE TABBY DEVON REX

WHITE DEVON REX

CHARACTERISTICS
The Devon Rex is a lively, playful, acrobatic cat but is a bit less active than the Cornish Rex. Naturally cheerful and independent, Devon Rexes are friendly toward other cats and toward dogs. They hate being left alone.
Very affectionate and sensitive, they are pleasant companions with soft, quiet voices. They are well-suited to apartment life, as they are susceptible to cold. Kittens develop quickly. The coat does not attain its adult appearance until about 6 months.
Daily brushing is enough to maintain the Devon's coat. Devons hardly shed at all. They must be bathed regularly, since they sweat and their ears produce a great deal of wax.
The pedigree should be examined closely in order to avoid the risk of spasticity.

(▼)F.I.Fe　(■) L.O.O.F.　(★) C.F.A.　(◆) T.I.C.A.

European Shorthair

Country of Origin: Continental Europe
Other Name: European

A commoner with a pedigree!

The European Shorthair is the Continental European equivalent to the British Shorthair in Great Britain and the American Shorthair in the United States. The European Shorthair is derived from the common domestic cat (house cat or mixed breed cat) through selective breeding based on aesthetic criteria.

In 1925, so-called "European" cats obtained their first standard. This breed, previously grouped with the British Shorthair, was approved by the F.I.Fe. in 1982. It is not recognized by Great Britain's G.C.C.F.

RIGHT: TABBY EUROPEAN SHORTHAIR

European Shorthair

GENERAL
Medium-limbed type (the British Shorthair is shorter-limbed).
Medium to large in size. Males can reach 8 kg.
Shorthaired.

BICOLOR

TORTOISESHELL, THREE COLORS

EARS
Medium-sized, slightly rounded at the tips, which may have lynx tips. Well-spaced and erect.

EYES
Large, round, widely spaced, set at a slight slant. Color must be clear and pure and correspond to that of the coat.

NECK
Moderately long and muscular.

BODY
Fairly long, not stout. Stocky, strong, muscular. Broad, well-developed chest.

LEGS AND PAWS
Moderately long, strong, solid, tapering evenly to the paws, which are round and firm.

TAIL
Moderately long, fairly thick at the base, tapering gradually to a rounded tip.

COAT
Short, dense, close-lying, lustrous hair without undercoat. All colors except chocolate, lilac, and colorpoint.

NOTES
Allowable outcross breeds: none.

FAULTS
Body too large or too stout. Strong resemblance to British Shorthair and American Shorthair. Pendulous cheeks. Clear stop. Long, wooly fur (▼).

BICOLOR

HEAD
Fairly broad with rounded contours but a bit longer than it is wide. Slightly rounded skull and forehead. Well-developed cheeks, especially in males. Straight, moderately long nose with no stop (■) and a clearly defined base (▼). Rounded, firm chin.

ORANGE TABBY

TABBY

CHARACTERISTICS
The European Shorthair is a hardy, active, dynamic, playful cat. More easygoing in nature than the mixed breed cat, the European Shorthair is calmer and gentler.
An affectionate, pleasant companion, it is highly adaptable. A good hunter, it likes being outdoors. It is easy to groom. Weekly brushing is quite sufficient, except during shedding.

(▼) F.I.Fe   (■) L.O.O.F.   (★) C.F.A.   (◆) T.I.C.A.

Exotic Shorthair

Country of Origin: United States

This feisty ball of fluff takes time to grow up

In the United States, around 1960, breeders crossed the American Shorthair with the Persian in order to improve the American's coat color and make it heavier. Thus were born shorthaired Persians, dubbed Exotic Shorthairs and recognized by the C.F.A in 1966.

During the breeding program, crosses were also made with the Russian Blue and the Burmese. Since 1987, the only allowable outcross breed is the Persian.

The F.I.Fe. recognized the Exotic Shorthair in 1986. Very common in the United States, Exotic Shorthairs are conquering Europe.

BROWN TABBY EXOTIC SHORTHAIR

Exotic Shorthair

CHINCHILLA EXOTIC SHORTHAIR

GENERAL
Shorthaired Persian.
Weight: 3 to 6.5 kg.
Medium-sized, short-limbed.

SILVER TABBY

BLUE CREAM TORTIE

Large, round, well-spaced. Pure, deep color corresponding to that of the coat (gold to copper in most varieties; green in the chinchilla and the golden; blue in the white and the colorpoint).

NECK
Short and thick.

BODY
Medium in size, cobby, low to the ground. Broad chest. Massive shoulders. Large-boned, powerful muscles.

LEGS AND PAWS
Short, straight, and large. Round, large paws. Tufts of hair between the toes are desirable.

erect hair. All Persian colors are recognized.

NOTES
Allowable outcross breed: Persian.

FAULTS
Head too long or too narrow. Nose too long or roman nose. Narrow, thin muzzle. Small, slanted, pale-colored eyes. Ears too large. Body too long or narrow. Narrow chest. Long, slender legs. Oval paws. Tail too long. Disqualify: lockets or spots (■).

HEAD
Round, massive. Very broad skull. Rounded forehead. Round, full cheeks. Short, broad, round muzzle. Short, broad nose with pronounced stop. Broad, open nostrils to facilitate air flow (▼). Strong chin. Broad, powerful jaws.

EARS
Small, rounded at the tip, not too open at the base. Widely spaced and well-furnished with hair on the inside.

EYES

TAIL
Short, thick, carried low. Rounded tip.

COAT
Shorthaired but slightly longer than that of other shorthaired breeds. Dense, fluffy,

TORTIE

TABBY AND WHITE KITTEN

CHARACTERISTICS
The Exotic Shorthair is a tranquil cat but a bit livelier than the Persian. Curious, playful, and even-tempered, it is friendly to other cats and to dogs. Easygoing and quiet, as it rarely meows, it does not like being left alone. It is affectionate and needs the tender presence of its owner. This sturdy cat does not reach maturity until around three years of age and enters puberty fairly late. When two Exotic Shorthairs are crossed, they may produce longhaired kittens called "Exotic Longhairs" by the C.F.A. and considered Persians in France.
Exotic Shorthairs are easy to groom. Weekly brushing and combing is sufficient. During shedding, they should be brushed and combed daily. Because of their fairly productive tear ducts, their eyes should be cleaned daily.

(▼) F.I.Fe   (■) L.O.O.F.   (★) C.F.A.   (◆) T.I.C.A.

28

German Rex

Wearing a full lambswool coat

The German Rex is the oldest known breed of curly-coated cat. It first appeared in 1946 in the home of Dr. Scheuer-Karpin but was actually developed from a stray adopted by breeders in 1951. Curly-coated kittens were obtained through crosses with the Cornish Rex. This proved that the two breeds had the same gene responsible for the mutation. Both the F.I.Fe. and the L.O.O.F recognize the German Rex. However, the C.F.A. does not distinguish it from the Cornish Rex and Devon Rex. The German Rex is very rare.

BROWN TABBY

German Rex

GENERAL
Medium-sized, strong, muscular.

BLACK AND WHITE BICOLOR

WHITE WITH ORANGE EYES

HEAD
Rounded, very broad between the ears. Well-developed cheeks. Nose with a slight break at the base. Massive, strong chin. Curly whiskers, shorter than usual.

EARS
Medium-sized, broad at the base, with slightly rounded tips. Outside covered with fine, thick fur, inside slightly furry.

EYES
Medium-sized, well-spaced, and wide open. The color must be uniform and luminous, and must correspond to that of the coat.

BODY
Medium-sized, solid, muscular, but not massive or heavy. Rounded, powerful chest. The back is straight from the shoulders to the croup.

LEGS AND PAWS
Slender, moderately long. Well-developed,, slightly oval paws (*) with a rounded shape (▼).

TAIL
Moderately long, thick at the base and tapering to a rounded tip. Thick fur.

COAT
Short, velvety, soft, very silky. Must be wavy or curly. Curly over the entire body, longer than that of the Cornish Rex, more spiky. No guard hairs. Colors: all are recognized, except chocolate, lilac, and colorpoint.

NOTES
Allowable outcross breeds: none.

FAULTS
Head too long, too pointed. Small ears. Short, hairless tail. Shaggy coat , not wavy enough, with hairless patches (▼).

BROWN TABBY

TORTIE

CHARACTERISTICS
German Rexes are active but patient cats. They are even-tempered, friendly toward other cats, and very affectionate toward their owner. They are easy to groom.

(▼)F.I.Fe   (■) L.O.O.F.   (★) C.F.A.   (◆) T.I.C.A.

32

Havana

Country of Origin: Great Britain
Original Name: Havana Brown
Other Name(s): Chestnut Brown Foreign,
Chestnut Oriental Shorthair

Either a chestnut or lilac coat, but always green-eyed

*I*n the early 19th century in England, a female chestnut brown cat named Granny Grump was reported. Much later, around 1880, other cats of the same color were successfully shown.

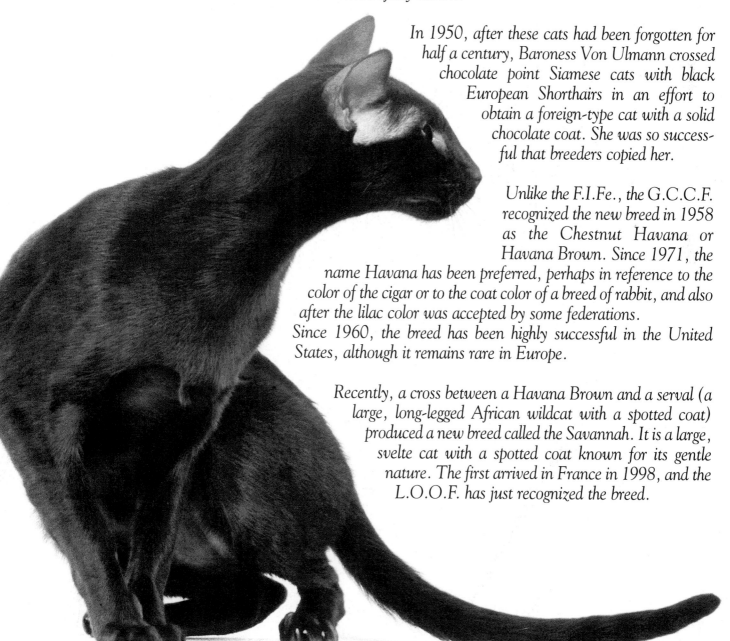

In 1950, after these cats had been forgotten for half a century, Baroness Von Ulmann crossed chocolate point Siamese cats with black European Shorthairs in an effort to obtain a foreign-type cat with a solid chocolate coat. She was so successful that breeders copied her.

Unlike the F.I.Fe., the G.C.C.F. recognized the new breed in 1958 as the Chestnut Havana or Havana Brown. Since 1971, the name Havana has been preferred, perhaps in reference to the color of the cigar or to the coat color of a breed of rabbit, and also after the lilac color was accepted by some federations.

Since 1960, the breed has been highly successful in the United States, although it remains rare in Europe.

Recently, a cross between a Havana Brown and a serval (a large, long-legged African wildcat with a spotted coat) produced a new breed called the Savannah. It is a large, svelte cat with a spotted coat known for its gentle nature. The first arrived in France in 1998, and the L.O.O.F. has just recognized the breed.

Havana

GENERAL
Medium-sized.
Weight: 2.5 to 4.5 kg.
English type: long-limbed.
American type: medium-limbed (♦).

HEAD
Longer than it is wide. English version: Oriental type without whisker pinch or stop. American version: slightly triangular with significant pinch and stop (♦). Slightly rounded skull. Jowls allowed in adult males. Long, angular muzzle. Strong, angular, firm chin.

EARS
Large, rounded at the tip, widely spaced. Pointed forward when alert. Very little fur, especially on the inside.

EYES
Large, oval, not globular, set near the bridge of the nose. Colors: all shades and intensities of green. A change in color is allowed until the age of one year.

NECK
Medium in size and length.

BODY
Medium in size and bone structure. Medium-limbed (American type) or long-limbed (English type). Firm muscles.

LEGS AND PAWS
Long, slender but not too thin. Compact, oval paws.

TAIL
Moderately long, not too thick at the base, tapering toward the tip.

COAT
Short, fine, silky, lying flat against the body. Very thick undercoat. Slightly fluffier fur allowed for lilac coats (♦). Colors:
- chocolate: chestnut brown, solid hazelnut brown. Brown whiskers and nose leather, pink paw pads. The C.F.A.

recognizes this color only.
- lilac: taupe with pink highlights. T.I.C.A. recognizes both these colors.

Kittens are born with tabby ghost markings that disappear during the first year.

NOTES
Allowable outcross breeds: none.

FAULTS
Absence of break in the muzzle. Absence of chin. Kinked tail. Disqualify: wrong eye color. White markings.

CHARACTERISTICS
Havanas are lively, active, and playful but not aggressive cats. Standoffish toward strangers, they like tranquility and comfort. Calm, affectionate, and very gentle, they adore their owner. Less talkative than the Siamese, they also have a softer voice. In terms of grooming, weekly brushing is sufficient for this breed.

(▼)F.I.Fe   (■) L.O.O.F.   (★) C.F.A.   (♦) T.I.C.A.

Japanese Bobtail

A pompom tail and a tricolor coat

These worshipped cats might have originated in China, then Japan, as they appear on many artifacts and prints from as early as the 11th century from several far eastern countries. In that long-ago era, only the royal family and the aristocracy owned cats of this breed.
Highly honored and even venerated (especially the tricolor or "Mi-ke" variety), a symbol of luck and happiness, these cats are depicted with the front right paw raised (Maneki-neko means "waving cat") in art found in Japanese homes and temples.

The breed's bobbed tail is a characteristic determined by a recessive autosomal gene. In 1968, the first Japanese Bobtails were imported to the United States by the breeder E. Freret, who started a breeding program. The C.F.A. published a standard in 1971. The F.I.Fe. recognized the breed in 1990. In 1981, the female Sirikit and the male Aikido became the first Japanese Bobtails imported to France. Highly popular in the United States, the breed remains very rare in France.

Japanese Bobtail

TRICOLOR AND BICOLOR

GENERAL
Medium-sized. Well-muscled body that is long and svelte, rather than massive.
Tail curled like a pompom.
Weight: 2.5 to 4 kg.

EARS
Large, straight, well-spaced, never facing outward. At rest, appear to be slanted forward.

EYES
Large, oval, wide open. Appear clearly slanted in profile. Color corresponding to that of the coat.

BODY
Long, svelte, well-muscled without appearing heavy.

HEAD
Appears long and chiseled, shaped like an equilateral triangle with soft curves. High, prominent cheekbones. Jowls are allowed in unaltered males. Whisker pinch. Long, well-defined nose with a slight depression at or just below the eyes. Fairly broad muzzle, neither pointed nor flat, rounding in a slight break at the whiskers. Well-marked whisker pads (◆).

The tail may consist of one or more sections; if it has several sections, it is curled and angled. Hairs longer and thicker than that on the body give the tail a pompom appearance (▼).

COAT
Short or semilong, soft, silky but without a true undercoat.
Two varieties:
- shorthaired
- semilonghaired or longhaired. Possible ruff.

All colors are recognized except chocolate, lilac,

FAULTS
Short, round head. Stout, massive body. Absence of bones in the tail; tail too straight, standing out too much from the body. Absence of pompom.

LEGS AND PAWS
Long and thin but not delicate or fragile. The hind legs are clearly longer than the forelegs. Oval paws.

TAIL
Maximum tail length is 5 to 8 cm, although when fully extended it can reach 10 to 13 cm. The bones are large, rigid, virtually fused (except at the base).

and colorpoint. Tricolors and bicolors are among the preferred patterns. The Mi-ke (tricolor black, reddish-brown, and white cat that produces only females) is the most prized. Patterns should be clear and well-marked, and colors should be even.

NOTES
Allowable outcross breeds: none.

CHARACTERISTICS
The lively, extraverted, independent, and curious Japanese Bobtail has a strong personality, like all Oriental-type cats. Not always friendly toward other cats, it usually ignores dogs.
The very playful Japanese Bobtail gets along well with children. It is talkative and "sings" in a soft voice. Very affectionate, it is highly attached to its owner.
Well-balanced thanks to an excellent character, Japanese Bobtails adapt well to both apartment and outdoor life. Athletic hunters, they are crazy about water.
In terms of grooming, they require only weekly brushing. They shed very little.

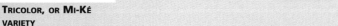

TRICOLOR, OR MI-KÉ VARIETY

Javanese

Country of Origin: United States

Like the Oriental Shorthair or the Balinese, but with semilong hair

Despite its name, this cat did not originate in Java. During breeding programs that led to the creation of the Balinese (semilonghaired Siamese), American breeders obtained a semilonghaired Oriental called the Javanese because of its type.

Feline associations are divided on the issue of whether the Javanese is truly a new breed or simply a variety of Balinese. The F.I.Fe., for example, considers it a semilonghaired Oriental type with a solid coat and green eyes. The C.F.A. considers the Javanese simply as a Balinese with coloring other than the four recognized basic colors (seal, blue, chocolate, and lilac point). The Javanese is therefore a colorpoint with dark blue eyes like the Siamese.

The Javanese is still quite rare in Europe.

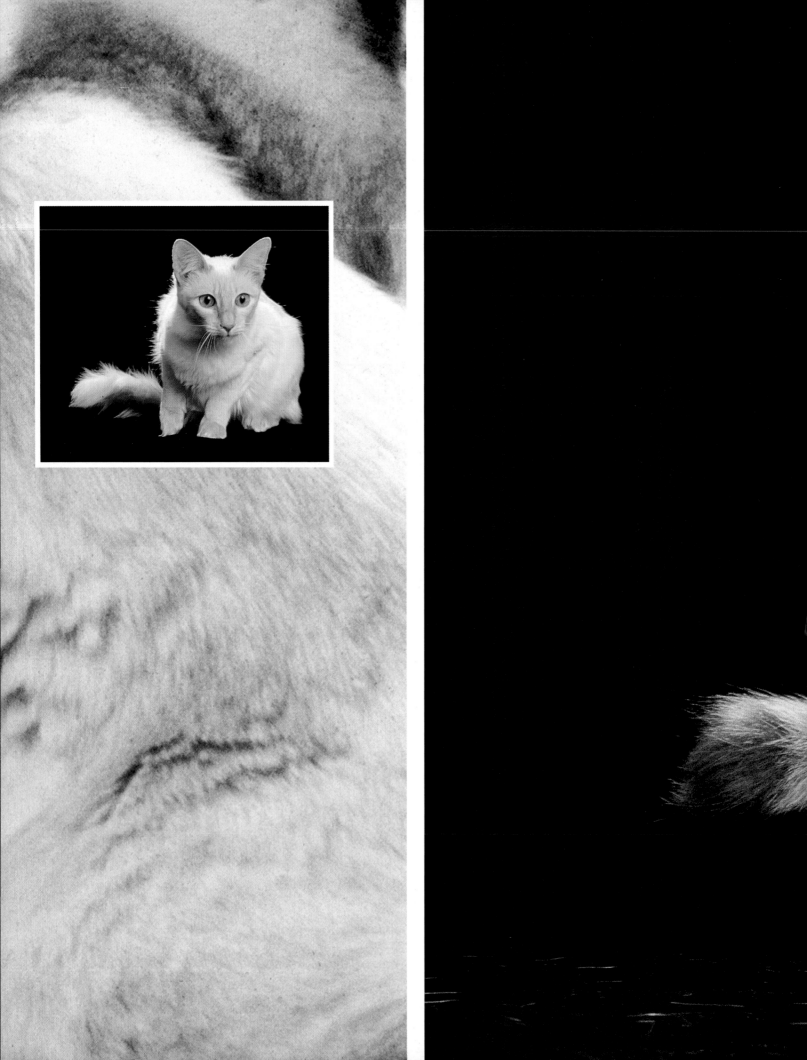

Javanese

GENERAL
Medium-sized, but heavier than the Siamese (∗).
Svelte, long-limbed, elegant but muscular cat (▼).

HEAD
Medium-sized, can be inscribed in a triangle. In profile, the skull is slightly convex. Slender muzzle. Long, straight nose continuing the line of the forehead without break. Medium-sized chin.

EARS
Large, broad at the base, pointed. They extend the sides of the triangle.

EYES
Medium-sized, almond-shaped, set slightly at a slant toward the nose. Color: luminous green (▼). Colorpoints and white-coated cats have dark blue eyes (∗).

NECK
Long and slender.

BODY
Long, svelte, graceful but muscular.

LEGS AND PAWS
Long, slender, in proportion to the body. Small, oval paws.

TAIL
Very long and slender, even at the base, tapering to the tip.

COAT
Thin, silky hair moderately long on the body, slightly longer on the ruff, shoulders, and tail (plume). No wooly undercoat (▼).

Even color without tabby markings or shading in non-agouti varieties. Varieties are those of the Oriental type. The eyes are green, except in the white-coated Javanese, which has dark blue eyes (▼).Colorpoint with dark blue eyes, in the varieties recognized for the Siamese (∗).

FAULTS
White markings. Eyes more yellow than green (▼). Tabby markings in non-agouti varieties.

CHARACTERISTICS
The Javanese has the character and temperament of an Oriental type cat. Javanese cats are extraverted and "talk" a lot in a melodious voice.
  They are possessive, following their owner like a small dog, and they know how to get all the petting they want.
They are also athletes and excellent hunters. They are easy to groom, especially since they love being brushed.

(▼) F.I.F.e   (■) L.O.O.F.   (★) C.F.A.   (◆) T.I.C.A.

44

Korat

Country of Origin: Thailand
Original Name: Si-sawat

This independent gray cat brings good luck

This natural breed originated in Thailand, where it was first established in the 14th century. It is named after a province in Thailand, where it is considered a bearer of good luck. In fact, its original name, Si-sawat, means culture and prosperity.

In The Cat Book of Poems of the Ayutthaya kingdom (1350-1767), this cat is said to have "eyes that shine like dewdrops on a lotus leaf."

Specimens were imported and shown in Great Britain in the late 19th century, but without success, since they were seen simply as Siamese cats with blue coats.

American breeder Jean Johnson began breeding Korats in 1959. The breed was recognized by the C.F.A. in 1966 and by T.I.C.A. in 1969.

Upon its arrival in Europe in 1972, the Korat was approved by the F.I.Fe. Well-known in the United States, the breed is quite uncommon in Europe.

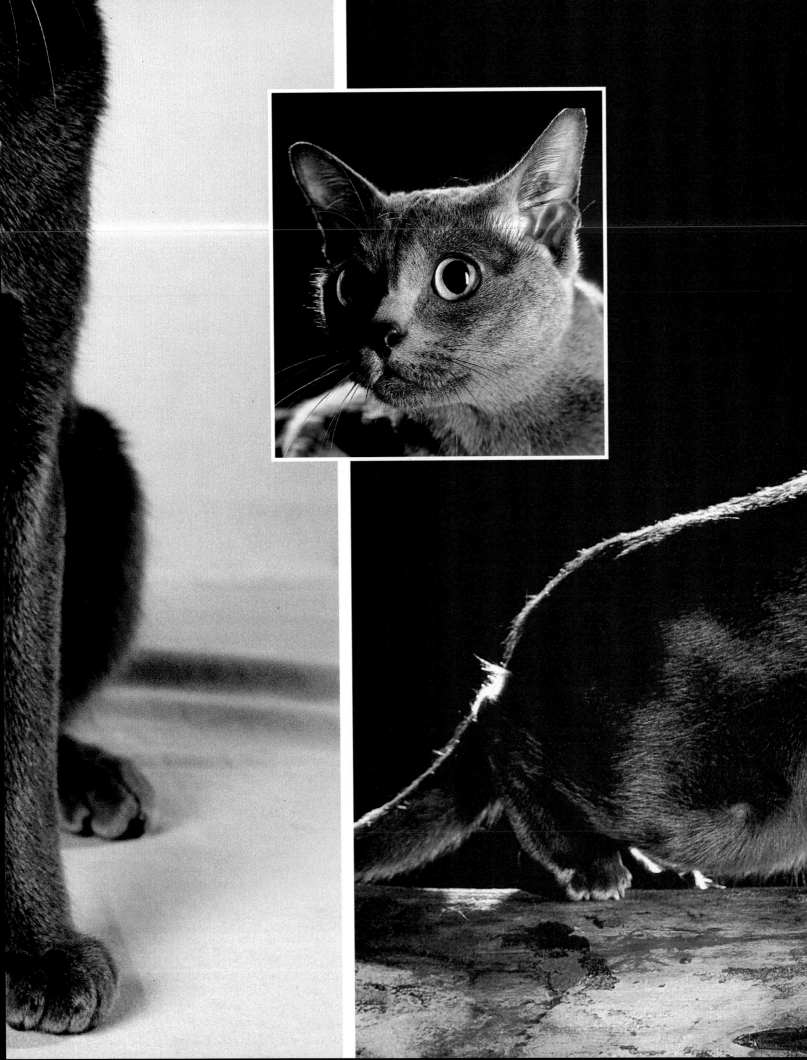

Korat

GENERAL
Medium-sized, semi-cobby body, fairly medium-limbed.
Weight: 2.5 to 4.5 kg.
Shorthaired.

SILVER BLUE

HEAD
Heart-shaped when seen from the front. Flat forehead. Slight stop between the forehead and nose. Firm, well-developed cheeks. Muzzle neither pointed nor angular. Long nose, slightly domed at the tip. Strong, well-developed chin. Strong jaws.

EARS
Large, broad at the base with slightly rounded tips. Set high on the skull, on alert. Short hair on the outside.

EYES
Large, round, well-spaced, slightly slanted. Preferably luminous green in color. Amber eyes are accepted, especially in young cats (▼). Actually, the final color is not attained before the age of two. Eyebrows form two broad curves above the eyes.

NECK
Medium-sized, long.

BODY
Medium-sized, semi-cobby, neither compact nor svelte (★). Slightly

arched back. Strong, muscular, flexible.

LEGS AND PAWS
Hind legs slightly longer than forelegs. Medium to heavy bone structure. Oval paws.

TAIL
Moderately long, thicker at the base, tapering to a rounded tip.

COAT
Short, fine, lustrous, dense hair. Simple coat (no undercoat) tending to stand erect on the spine when the cat is in motion. Even, silver blue

color (★). The tip of the hair is silver, making the coat appear frosted (◆). The nose leather is dark blue-gray. Paw pads dark blue to pinkish lavender.

NOTES
Allowable outcross breeds: none.

FAULTS
Narrow head. Small, closely spaced eyes. Yellow eyes (◆). Nose too long or too short. Pinched chin. Disqualify: any color other than blue. White markings.

CHARACTERISTICS
The Korat is lively, active, very agile and playful but does not like agitation or noise. It needs a tranquil environment. Korats are not very friendly toward other cats and are reserved toward strangers. Gentle, very affectionate, and hypersensitive, they are highly attached to their owner. They need lots of love and attention. They have a melodious voice. They are easy to groom, as weekly brushing is sufficient.

(▼) F.I.Fe   (■) L.O.O.F.   (★) C.F.A.   (◆) T.I.C.A.

48

La Perm

Country of Origin: United States
Original Name: Dalles La Perm

With or without hair!

I n 1982 in an orchard in The Dalles, Oregon, a cat owned by Linda Koehl had a litter of six kittens, including a female named Curly. Curly was born hairless; two months later she had a curly, silky coat.

For five years, Koehl raised many other curly-coated cats who are the ancestors of the Dalles La Perm breed, the result of a spontaneous mutation by a dominant gene.

T.I.C.A. recognized the breed and published a standard in 1996.

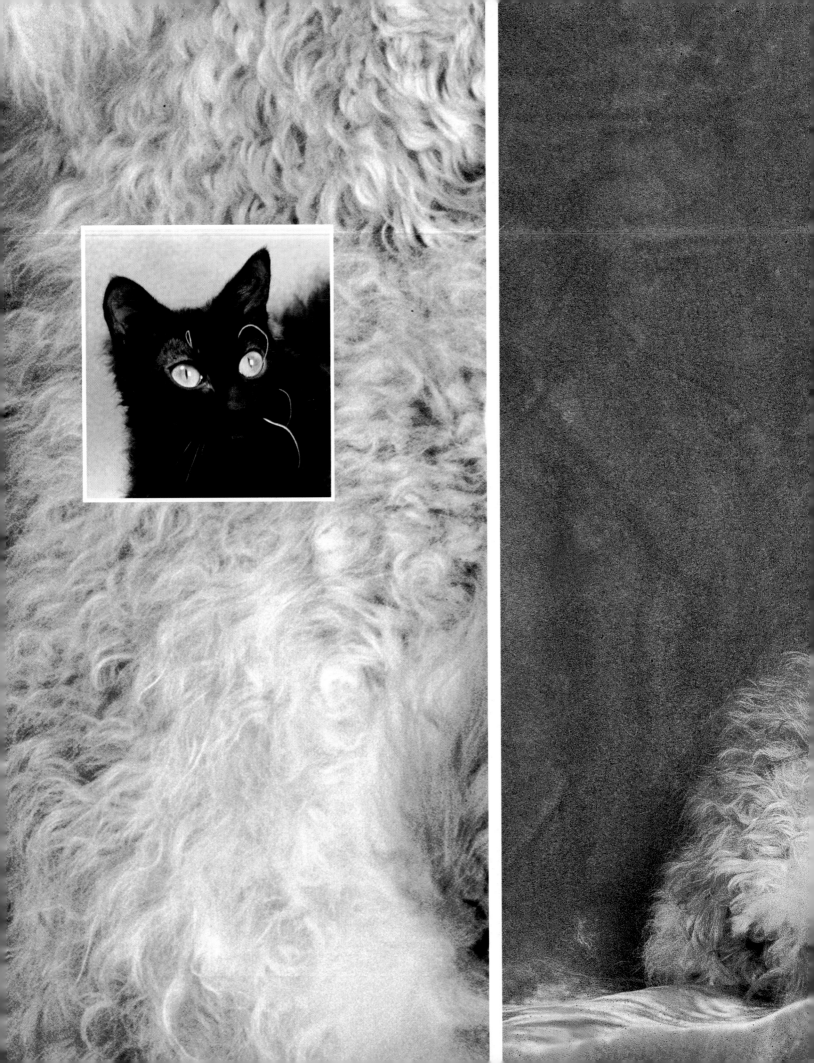

La Perm

GENERAL
Medium-sized, semi-foreign type with a curly coat.
Weight: 3.5 to 5.5 kg.

EYES
Large, almond-shaped, moderately spaced. No relationship between eye color and coat color.

NECK
Moderately long; carried high.

BODY
Semi-foreign type, medium-sized. Surprisingly heavy for its size. Medium bone structure, fairly muscular (■)(◆).

HEAD
Triangular shape with rounded contours. Rounded skull. The profile presents a slight stop. High cheeks. Moderately long nose. Moderately prominent muzzle. Full, pronounced whisker pads. Firm chin (■)(◆).

EARS
Medium-sized, broad at the base with rounded tips. The inside surface is well-furnished with curly hair at the bottom of the ear. Lynx tips are desirable (■)(◆).

LEGS AND PAWS
Moderately long. Forelegs shorter than hind legs. Medium-boned. Fairly muscular. Round paws (■)(◆).

TAIL
Long and slender. Wavy fur.

COAT
Two varieties:
- shorthaired coat: soft, silky texture, wavy on the back and belly.

the ears. Disqualify: thin, angular body. Short legs.

Moderate undercoat.
- semilonghaired or longhaired coat: soft and curly texture. Heavy undercoat. Ruff accepted in adults. Whiskers and hair inside the ears may be curly.
These cats are hairless at least once in their life, often when they are very young. The coat often grows back curly. Colors: all are allowed.

NOTES
Outcrossing with other breeds allowed as long as the population is insufficient (■).

FAULTS
No hair in the ears. No long, curly hair below

CHARACTERISTICS
This extraverted, curious farm cat is an excellent hunter and good companion. It has a soft voice.

(▼) F.I.Fe.   (■) L.O.O.F.   (★) C.F.A.   (◆) T.I.C.A.

Domestic Lynx

Country of Origin: United States

A tame little wild cat

This new breed was created in the 1980s in the United States by crossing the small bobcat and Canadian lynx with domestic cats. "The ideal in breeding is a cat as similar as possible either to the bobcat or to the Canadian lynx or jungle cat (*Felis chaus*), with the gentle, trusting nature of a domestic cat" (■). The Domestic Lynx is still very rare.

BROWN SPOTTED TABBY

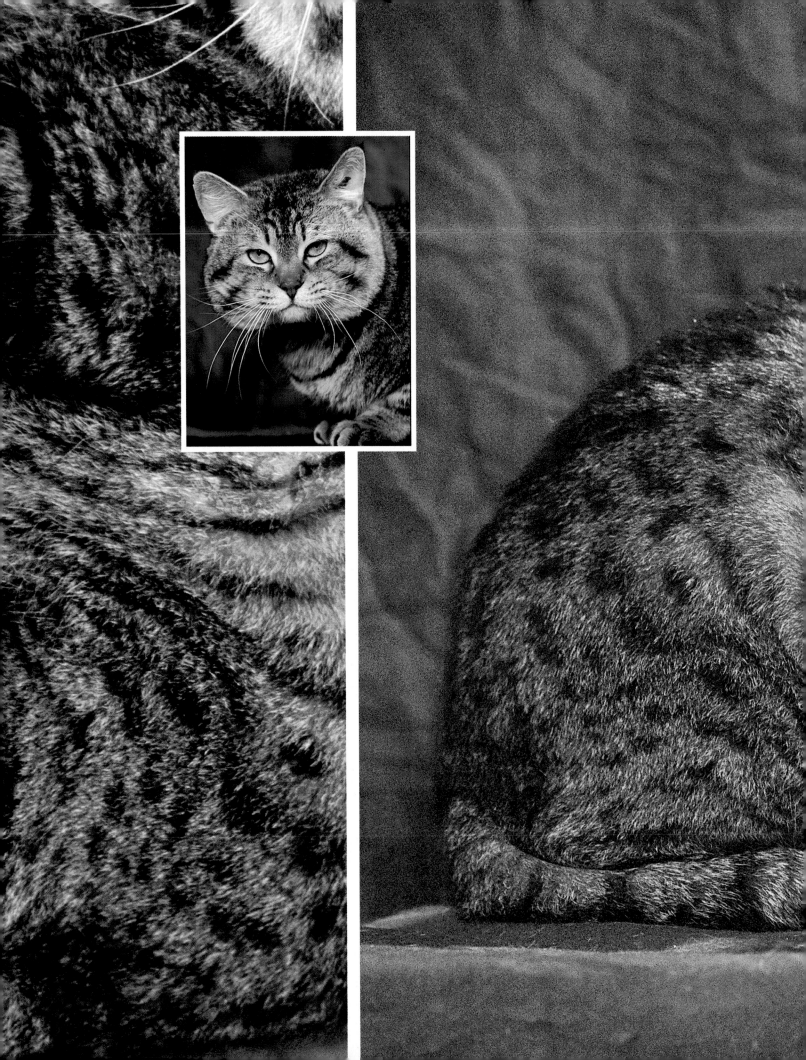

Domestic Lynx

GENERAL
Powerful, fairly long-legged cat with a heavy bone structure and well-developed muscles. Males are much larger and stronger than females.

HEAD
Triangular in shape. Slightly concave profile without a clear break. High cheekbones. Angular muzzle. Nose moderately long and very broad. Strong chin. Relatively short, very powerful jaws (■).

EYES
Almond-shaped, slightly slanted. All colors are allowed. Blue eyes in the colorpoint (■).

BODY
Large in size, rectangular in shape. Slightly curved back.

EARS
Medium-sized, broad at the base, pointed, set high. Covered with hair and preferably having lynx tips.

LEGS AND PAWS
Long, massive. Hind legs are slightly longer than forelegs. Round paws. Hair between the paw pads.

TAIL
Short like that of the wild lynx. Its minimum length of 10 cm should not extend below the knee. It must be flexible.

COAT
Short to semilong coat. Longer on the belly and thighs. A ruff or beard is preferable. Thick, silky texture with a heavy, nearly waterproof undercoat.

All eumelanistic colors: black, blue, cinnamon, fawn, chocolate, lilac, either in a light or dark shade or in combination with the silver factor for spotted and ticked patterns only, or the above colors in a colorpoint pattern (■).
Typical agouti markings on the forehead and face. The legs are striped or, preferably, spotted. Well-defined spots on the belly. The tail is ringed with a black tip. Reddish-brown and tortoiseshell coloring do not exist in this breed. There is also a "snow" version, that is, with blue eyes and Siamese markings on a light, spotted body.

NOTES
Allowable outcross breeds: European Shorthair, Maine Coon, American Shorthair (■).

FAULTS
Disqualify: reddish-brown coloring. White markings. Tail too short or too long.

TABBY

CHARACTERISTICS
This cat is gentle and sociable. It gets along well with dogs but is rather dominant toward other cats. The affectionate Domestic Lynx makes a good pet.

(▼)F.I.Fe   (■) L.O.O.F.   (★) C.F.A.   (◆) T.I.C.A.

Oriental Longhair

A refined Oriental type with a long coat

This semilonghaired Oriental type was obtained recently by crossing Oriental Shorthairs and Balinese (longhaired Siamese). Today, American breeders continue to cross Oriental Shorthairs, Balinese, and Siamese in order to better establish the new breed's characteristics.

The Oriental Longhair received provisional recognition from the C.F.A. in 1994. T.I.C.A. published a standard in 1998.

This breed is still rare in Europe.

Oriental Longhair

GENERAL
Svelte, refined, very flexible but strong and muscular cat.
Its body is thicker than that of the Oriental Shorthair.
Weight: 4.5 to 6 kg.

EYES
Medium-sized, almond-shaped, and slanted as in Oriental types.
Green or blue in white cats.

All Oriental Shorthair colors are recognized. Chocolate and lilac are the most desirable.

NOTES
Allowable outcross breeds: Oriental Shorthair, Siamese, and Balinese.

FAULTS
Round or broad head. Short or broad muzzle. Sloped nose. Small, round eyes without slant. Short body. Short coat. Absence of plume on the tail.

HEAD
Long and triangular. Flat forehead. Straight profile. Slender muzzle without break. Long, straight nose. Strong chin.

EARS
Very large but in proportion to the head.

NECK
Long, slender, and graceful.

BODY
Medium-sized and Oriental in type, that is, long and tubular. Fine-boned. Firm muscles.

LEGS AND PAWS
Long and slender. Hind legs longer than forelegs. Fine-boned. Slender, firm muscles. Small, oval paws.

TAIL
Long and well-furnished.

COAT
Semilong, fine, silky hair lying flat against the body. Thin undercoat. Shorter hair on the tops of the shoulders and head. Ruff and britches present. Plume on the tail.

TABBY

CHARACTERISTICS
These lively, energetic, playful cats with a strong personality are calmer and more even-tempered than the Oriental Shorthair.
Oriental Longhairs are sociable, getting along well with other cats, but reserved with strangers.
Very affectionate and highly attached to their owner, they are real "talkers" with a lovely voice. They do not like being left alone.
They are easy to groom.

 F.I.Fe   L.O.O.F.   (★) C.F.A.   (◆) T.I.C.A.

Manx

Country of Origin: Isle of Man
Original Name: Man's Cat
Other Name: Isle of Man Cat

A tailless cat that hops like a rabbit

This cat's name is derived from its native Isle of Man, off the coast of Ireland. These cats, described in China, Japan, Malaysia, and Russia, were once thought to be from the Far East. For example, they could have been brought by Spanish sailors after the wreck of a Spanish galleon in Philip II's invincible armada in 1588. Actually, the breed is the result of a spontaneous genetic mutation caused by a dominant autosomal gene (M) expressed in various ways: from tailless Manx cats (rumpies) to those with a normal tail (tailies).

Because of the high degree of inbreeding in the feline population on the small Isle of Man, the M gene was easily passed down through many generations. The Manx was very popular in England by the late 19th century. A Manx Club was created in Great Britain in 1901.

While very popular in countries including the United States and Great Britain, the Manx is quite uncommon in France.

A semilonghaired Manx called the Cymric has been selectively bred in North America.

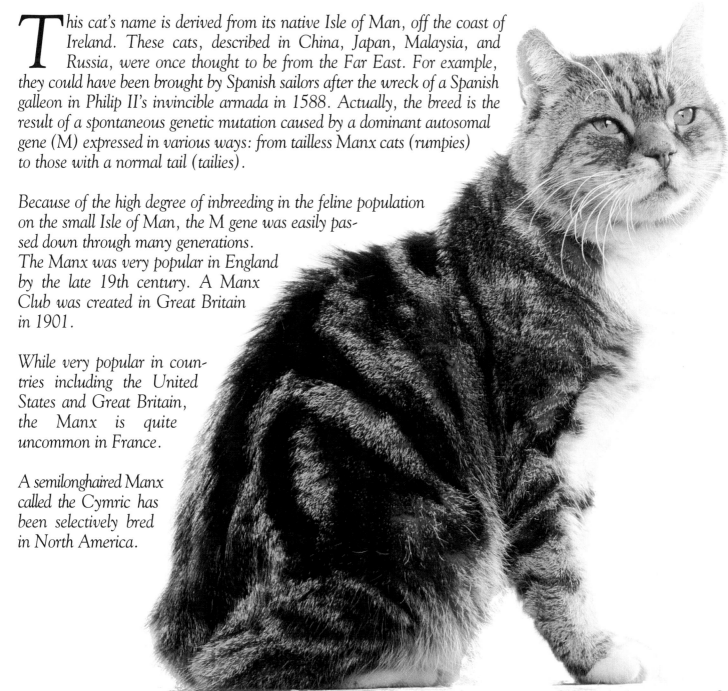

TORTOISESHELL BLOTCHED TABBY

Manx

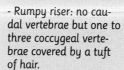

GENERAL
Medium-sized.
Weight: 3.5 to 5.5 kg.
Compact, fairly short-limbed.
Impression of roundness.

BROWN TABBY AND WHITE

HEAD
Relatively broad and round. Moderately rounded forehead. Prominent cheeks. Muzzle slightly longer than it is wide. Medium-sized nose without clear break, not turned up (▼). Well-developed, round whisker pads (◆). Strong chin. Large whiskers.

EARS
Medium-sized, broad at the base, rounded tips. Well-spaced. Sparse fur.

EYES
Large, round, slightly slanted (◆). Color corresponding to that of the coat.

NECK
Short, thick, powerful.

BODY
Medium-sized, solid, compact (cobby). Broad chest. Short, convex back. Croup very rounded and higher than shoulders. Heavy-boned. Muscular.

- Rumpy riser: no caudal vertebrae but one to three coccygeal vertebrae covered by a tuft of hair.
- Stumpy: tail several centimeters long, one to three caudal vertebrae, often with bone deformities ("kinked" tail).
- Taily: normal or kinked tail.

COAT
Short, dense, double coat (very thick undercoat). All colors and patterns are allowed, with or without white.

NOTES
Allowable outcross breeds: Cymric, British Shorthair (■).

FAULTS
Eyes not set at a slant. Long, slender body. Flat back. Short hind legs. Fine-boned. Disqualify: weakness in hindquarters (■).

CREAM AND WHITE KITTEN

RED AND WHITE KITTEN

LEGS AND PAWS
Forelegs shorter than hind legs. Heavy-boned and very muscular. Round paws. Hopping gait resembling that of a rabbit.

TAIL
Variety:
- Rumpy: tail absent (no caudal or coccygeal vertebrae). There must be a depression at the tail base.

RED BLOTCHED TABBY AND WHITE

CHARACTERISTICS
With its excellent character, this cat adapts easily to changes in lifestyle.
Manxes are sociable and accepting of other animals. Patient with children, they are affectionate toward their owner. Hardy, lively, and active, they are good hunters. Manx kittens grow slowly. Manxes are less prolific than average domestic cats, and they are difficult to breed. Homozygotic kittens (MM, carriers of two "doses" of the dominant mutant gene) die in the uterus (due to the incomplete development of the spinal cord). Thus, all Manxes are heterozygotic (Mm). Rumpies should not be bred together, due to the risk of this fatal gene combination. Instead, it is advised to breed Manxes with American Shorthairs or British Shorthairs, knowing that not all the kittens in each litter will be Manxes. Manxes are easy to groom.

(▼) F.I.Fe   (■) L.O.O.F.   (★) C.F.A.   (◆) T.I.C.A.

KNOWING
THE CAT

ANATOMY
PHYSIOLOGY
NUTRITION
GENETICS
PREVENTION
DISEASES

The Main Stages of a Cat's Life

*A cat's life expectancy is approximately ten years, although it is not uncommon
for cats to reach 15 and even 20 years old. From a kitten weighing 100 g at birth to
an adult weighing 2 to 7 kg (depending on the breed), a cat spends its life playing,
grooming, and sleeping, all of which is punctuated by meals.
Although a cherished companion, the cat retains its predatory instinct, evident even
in its play.*

Kitten grooming itself.

At Birth

After a gestation period of sixty-three to sixty-eight days, the female cat gives birth to a litter of one to ten kittens weighing 70 to 150 g each. The average birth weight is 100 g and varies according to a number of factors, including:

• Sex: Females are slightly lighter than males;
• Breed: Newborns of large breeds like the Norwegian Forest Cat are heavier than those of other breeds;

• Litter size: In litters of over five kittens, newborns are lighter.

• The mother's diet during gestation: If the mother's diet is unbalanced or insufficient, the fetuses can suffer from malnutrition, and she may produce lighter, weaker kittens that may even have birth defects.

From Birth to Adulthood

The mother cat licks each newborn kitten to remove the membrane that envelopes it. This licking behavior continues well beyond birth, as mothers lick their kittens to stimulate and awaken them. The first thing a kitten does after birth is to seek its mother's teats.

THE MOTHER'S MILK

In the first few days following birth, the mother cat lies on her side to make her teats accessible to her young. The kittens' first attempts at suckling produce not milk but colostrum, a substance different from milk in appearance and composition. In particular, colostrum contains numerous antibodies that the kitten absorbs in massive quantities during the first sixteen hours of life. These antibodies protect the kitten from germs in its environment for a few days to a few weeks. A few days later, the mother begins producing milk for her nursing kittens. Like colostrum, feline mother's milk is high in antibodies. For this reason, when kittens do not receive colostrum, they should be given feline mother's milk within sixteen hours of birth so that they can absorb the antibodies. Still, colostrum is always preferable, since, in addition to antibodies, it contains other elements lacking in milk.

At birth, kittens cannot regulate their body temperature and are thus very fragile and highly dependent on their mother to keep the nest warm. The rectal temperature of very young kittens is approximately 37°C, rising gradually to 38 to 38.5°C by the age of seven weeks. Thus, it is best to heat the queening box to 33°C the first week after birth and 30°C in the following weeks, decreasing the temperature to 28°C around the fourth or fifth week after birth and 26°C thereafter.

The Kitten's Development

A kitten acquires many abilities between birth and adulthood. The major changes occur before weaning, while the kittens are still nursing.

The Five Senses

At birth, the kitten already has a sense of smell keen enough to find its mother from a distance of 50 cm. Similarly, it is able to distinguish the three basic flavors: sweet, salty, and bitter (it dislikes salty and bitter). However, kittens are born blind and deaf. They acquire the senses of sight and hearing almost simultaneously.

Hearing develops when the kittens are around five days old, but they cannot orient themselves to sound until they are about fourteen days old. They do not have the hearing ability of an adult until the age of one month, at which time they learn to recognize their mother's voice.

Kittens first open their eyes seven to fifteen days after birth and acquire depth perception three or four days later. The simultaneous acquisition of sight and hearing requires a few days of adaptation.

Although far from nimble, kittens have a sense of balance from a very early age. They have difficulty coordinating their movements before they are two weeks old. They begin walking on four legs at around seventeen days old and are agile enough to scratch an ear with a hind leg around three weeks old.

Dental Development

It is fairly easy to determine a cat's age based on the date when baby and adult teeth first appear, since one needs only to open its mouth (see table at right).

Main Areas of the Body

Not all the main areas of the body develop at the same rate. Kittens are born with a relatively large head; then the limbs grow longer, making the kitten look quite tall and gangly. Finally, the rest of the body catches up, eventually attaining typical adult proportions.

ERUPTION OF TEETH IN KITTENS

	Deciduous Teeth (weeks)	Permanent Teeth
Incisors		
1st	2 to 3	3$^{1/2}$ to 4 months
2nd	2 to 4	3$^{1/2}$ to 4 months
3rd	3 to 4	4 to 4$^{1/2}$ months
Canines		
	3 to 4	5 months
Premolars		
2nd		4$^{1/2}$ to 5 months
3rd		5 to 6 months
4th		5 to 6 months
Molars		
1st		4 to 5 months

DIGESTIVE CAPACITIES

At birth, the kitten has a digestive tract adapted to digesting mother's milk. Feline mother's milk is rich in protein, fat, and lactose, or milk sugar. Thanks to an enzyme called lactase, the kitten is able to digest this lactose. Gradually, the kitten's digestive capacities change. Thus, many adult cats, having lost this enzyme, are unable to digest lactose and therefore milk. Undigested lactose travels through the small intestine to the large intestine, where bacteria cause it to ferment. This fermentation leads to acidic diarrhea.

As the ability to digest the lactose in milk decreases, the kitten gradually acquires other enzymes, including amylase, the enzyme enabling the digestion of starches.

The significant contribution of protein to the caloric value of feline milk is an early precursor in kittens to the strictly carnivorous diet of adult cats. Because cats cannot store protein, they require a great deal of protein in their diet.

Female cats nurse their kittens until they are six to seven weeks old, but kittens acquire the ability to chew and digest solid food around four to five weeks old. At this age, kittens tend naturally to begin nursing less often.

CHANGE IN FELINE DIGESTIVE CAPACITIES AS A FUNCTION OF AGE.

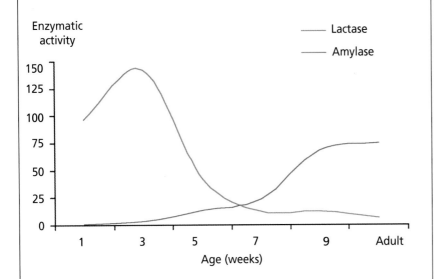

Example of lactase, the enzyme enabling the digestion of lactose (milk sugar) and amylase, the enzyme enabling the digestion of starch (Kienzle, 1987 and 1993).

Kitten Growth

A kitten's growth can be gauged by measuring its weight gain, an easy parameter to record. All kittens in the litter must be weighed every day at the same time. By recording this measurement, we can see the change in weight for each kitten and also compare kittens to each other.

A kitten should gain weight every day. There are a few guidelines for determining whether a kitten is developing properly. If the kitten does not gain weight for two consecutive days or if it loses weight, we must determine the cause: insufficient feeding by the mother, illness, etc. Normal growth in kittens from birth to adulthood occurs in three phases:

• **The neonatal period**, or approximately the first four days after birth, during which the rate of growth is highly variable, particularly with relation to birthing conditions. Kittens that had a difficult birth may stay at the same weight, but weight loss is rare.

• **During the strict nursing** period of the first four weeks, growth is regular and linear, and it is even possible to predict weight as a function of age. Thus, the weight at seven to ten days is equal to twice the birth weight, and the weight at four weeks is equal to four times the birth weight.

Growth during the strict nursing period is directly dependent on the quality of lactation and the mother's care of her kittens.

• **The pre-weaning period** is a time of dietary transition occurring when kittens are four to seven weeks old. At approximately four to five weeks old, the kittens' growth rate declines; this corresponds to a decrease in lactation associated with temporary undereating. Around the seventh week, another growth spurt occurs, indicating the end of weaning: The kitten is now consuming enough solid food for its growth to continue. Even during

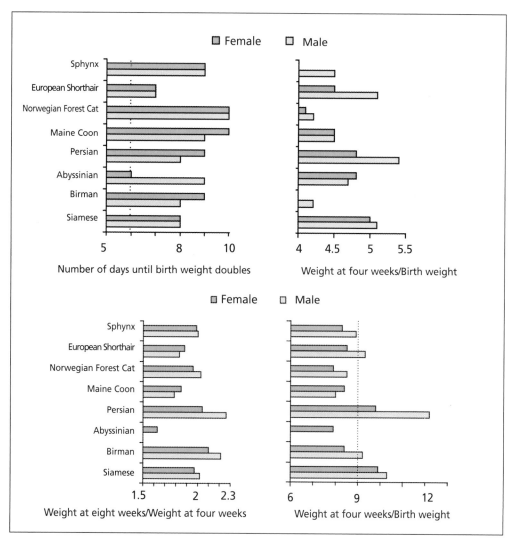

STANDARDS FOR GROWTH DURING THE STRICT NURSING PERIOD IN VARIOUS FELINE BREEDS, FOR BOTH SEXES *(Dubos, 1997).*

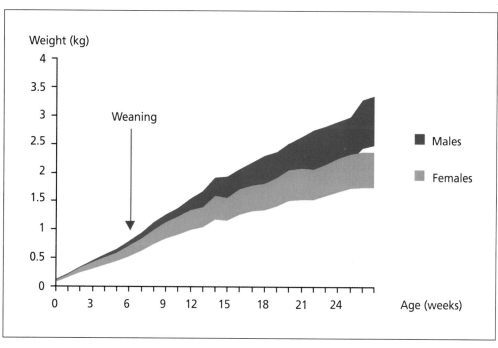

EXAMPLE OF GROWTH CURVE FOR KITTENS *(Siamese and Oriental) (Dubos, 1997).*

this transition period, the kitten continues to gain weight. The weight at eight weeks is generally equal to twice the weight at four weeks, or eight times the birth weight.

• **The post-weaning period** starting after eight weeks signals the beginning of the kitten's autonomy and corresponds to the expression of genetic potentialities. Individual variation is fully expressed at this time. The kitten eats by itself when it wants and grows to its full adult size. Once the cat reaches full size around ten to twelve months, it should maintain a constant weight.

Factors Influencing Kitten Growth

Among the factors influencing kitten growth are intrinsic factors determined by genetics (breed, sex, gene pool of the parents, hormonal mechanisms) and extrinsic factors involving the environment in a broad sense. These extrinsic factors are based essentially on the mother's and then the kitten's diet and are tempered by health and social conditions (breeding, living space, and maternal behavior).

Intrinsic factors include:

• Breed: As for most living species, the heavier the breed, the faster the growth.

• Sex: Sexual dimorphism is highly indistinct at birth and increases with age. Males become significantly heavier than females between six and twelve weeks old. Males thus have a higher growth potential than females, but this potential is delayed, with growth in males lasting a few weeks longer than in females.

• Family factors: Kittens receive half their genetic material from their mother and half from their father, with all this material being reworked to a certain extent. Family traits within a single breed may result in individuals that tend toward obesity or have a particular body size or type. These factors are especially important in selective breeding.

• The mother's weight: This parameter is not independent of breed and family factors. The heavier the mother (large in size and healthy), the faster the growth. This is explained partly by the quality of the mother's milk.

GROWTH AS A FUNCTION OF THE MOTHER'S WEIGHT. FACTORS INFLUENCING VARIATIONS IN WEIGHT

(Loveridge, 1987).

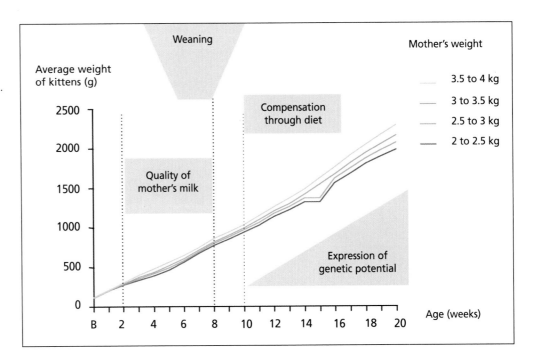

• Individual genetic factors: The combination of the maternal and paternal genotypes produces a unique individual and leads to individual variation within a single litter. Thus, to better estimate a kitten's growth, it is best to use the average of the parents' measurements.

• Hormonal factors: Following birth, certain hormones synthesized in the kitten's body guide its growth. Unlike humans, kittens rarely suffer from endogenous hormonal disorders that affect growth. Juvenile diabetes is marked by metabolic disorders, rather than growth disorders. Hypothyroidism is very rare, and dwarfism is unusual. Finally, the rare defects that result in the abnormal secretion of sex hormones seem to have little effect on growth in kittens. In addition, early spaying or neutering alters neither weight nor stature development, that is, growth to full adult size. However, the use of hormone therapy in kittens can greatly upset the natural endocrine balance and thus modify growth. This type of treatment should be used with great caution and for medical reasons only.

Many environmental factors determine successful growth.

• Hygiene of the cattery and surrounding stress

Nursing is a stressful period for the mother and a sensitive time for kittens. Strict hygiene must therefore be observed starting before birth and must involve both the equipment made available to the queen and the location of the queening box or nest. Inadequate hygiene will make the mother and her litter more susceptible to problems. In addition, when the mother is constantly disturbed, nursing suffers.

Just like for all young, a kitten's growth occurs during sleep. In the first few days of life, a young kitten sleeps almost constantly and nurses when awakened by its mother's licking. As it grows, the kitten will spend more time playing and exploring its environment, and less time sleeping. Still, the quality of its sleep

is very important. In addition, certain hormones secreted under stress can have a serious effect on hormonal balance and growth. Thus, a stressful environment can harm a kitten's well-being, as well as that of its mother, and can compromise growth that began under optimal conditions. The nest environment and the litter must be protected from disturbances in the home, excessive changes in temperature, unusual visits, etc.

• Litter size

Kittens in large litters normally weigh less than those in small litters. This weight disparity may even increase in the first weeks of life, since a large litter must share the same amount of mother's milk as a small litter. Kittens from large litters (six or more) are lighter until they are about two months old. It is only after weaning, when kittens receive a solid diet, that this disparity tends to lessen.

• Nutritional factors

The mother's diet during gestation influences the birth weight and viability of her kittens. From birth to weaning, a kitten's diet is composed only of mother's milk. The quality and quantity of this milk are therefore determining factors in kitten growth and health. Both the mother's and the kittens' diet must be considered.

Nursing queens have greatly increased dietary requirements. During gestation, the queen accumulates dietary reserves. At the start of nursing, her reserves are used for producing milk. Since the mother's body is focused primarily on milk production, if she is underfed she will begin by losing weight. Next, her milk production will decline.`

A queen allowed free access to food during gestation and lactation will recover her initial (pre-gestation) weight at weaning (six to seven weeks after the kittens are born). If the queen receives only 50% of her dietary requirements from five weeks before giving birth until the end of lactation, she will lose up to 33% her initial weight. The primary conse-

Cat milk

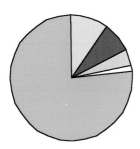

Cow's milk

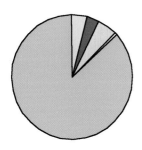

Human mother's milk

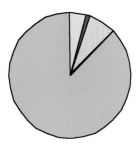

□ Fat
■ Protein
□ Lactose
□ Minerals
□ Water

RATIONAL DIET FOR THE NURSING QUEEN

Milk production requires a great deal of energy. For a kitten to gain one gram, it is estimated that it must ingest at least 2.7 g of milk. This means that during lactation, the queen must produce the equivalent of one and one-half to twice her own weight in milk. The dietary requirements of a nursing queen increase during lactation and are based on the number of kittens in the litter, although not proportionally.

A specially adapted, complete, and balanced food must therefore be offered freely to the mother. She must also have access to clean water at all times. A diet for lactating females must be richer than a maintenance diet. It must be higher in energy (calories), and therefore enriched in fat, but also in protein, taurine, and minerals, particularly calcium and phosphorus. Even with a specially adapted food, the queen cannot possibly consume the amount of food necessary to cover all these requirements, since they are so great. She will thus draw on the reserves her body built up during gestation. This phenomenon is normal and inevitable but need not be excessive. As a point of reference, let us note that a female cat gains approximately 40% her initial weight during gestation, still weighs 20% more after giving birth than before mating, and recovers her normal weight at the end of lactation. The queen's dietary consumption increases steadily throughout lactation until weaning is complete. Indeed, even though the kittens may nurse less and less frequently, the mother must rebuild her reserves and compensate for the losses incurred in the first phase of lactation.
In sum, the body prepares for lactation during gestation, and lactation continues based on the dietary contribution after birth.

VARIATION IN THE QUEEN'S FREE CONSUMPTION OF FOOD THROUGHOUT THE REPRODUCTIVE CYCLE.

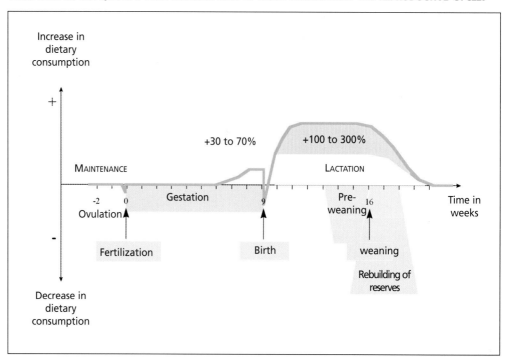

quence of this malnutrition is the queen's lack of attention toward her kittens—she becomes irritable when they try to nurse.

This change in the mother's behavior, combined with the kittens' malnutrition due to an insufficient milk supply, compromises the future of the litter.

The malnutrition of kittens during nursing has several possible causes: a malnourished mother, as we have just seen, but also highly insufficient lactation (very large litter, mother producing little milk) or insufficient nursing (mother not allowing sufficient nursing, too many kittens, stressful environment, not enough peace, etc.).

In all these cases, the kittens decline rapidly. Dehydration, hypoglycemia, and a decrease in body temperature are observed, and death follows. Several phenomena explain this very rapid decline:

• Because its liver is not yet mature, the kitten depends on glucose produced during the digestion of lactose from an external source (milk). In the case of underfeeding, hypoglycemia is inevitable and can lead to coma.

• A kitten's kidneys are immature at birth. The newborn is therefore not yet able to regulate the flow of water and minerals. Consequently, it must drink often, in small quantities. Any factor that limits nursing exposes kittens to rapid dehydration.

• Young kittens, especially newborns, are unable to regulate body temperature and fight temperatures that are too low because they do not have the necessary fat reserves. The steady, sufficient ingestion of milk and the mother's care during nursing (licking) and in the nest (mother's body heat) are essential to preventing hypothermia. The kittens' rectal temperature should thus be monitored, particularly if their weight remains the same from one day to the next.

Substitute Mother's Milk

When to Use
If the kittens are orphaned, if the litter is too large, or if the mother's milk cannot be consumed (due to a mammary condition), it may be necessary to administer a cat milk replacer. Feline mother's milk produces a certain amount of growth in kittens. Therefore, if the kittens do not gain weight over two consecutive days and no disease is detected, the mother's milk may be insufficient, with the kittens not receiving enough for growth. In this case, bottle feeding a milk replacer as a supplement to the mother's milk is a good solution for preparing all kittens in the litter for weaning.

How to Choose
Cat milk replacer, or substitute mother's milk, may be chosen based on various criteria:

• Composition of the milk. It is best to administer a type of milk that is as similar as possible to the mother's milk. Cat milk is fairly concentrated, similar to dog milk in composition, and much richer than cow's milk, particularly in fat, protein, and minerals.

Even though the composition of commercial substitute mother's milk is not always clearly indicated, a few guidelines can aid in making a selection. Kittens are adapted to digesting milk, that is, to digesting protein, fat, and lactose, all of animal origin. However, they are not yet well supplied with enzymes for digesting starch. Therefore, it is best to choose a milk with as little starch as possible, and, more generally, with as few ingredients of plant origin as possible (except oil, which provides essential fatty acids). The milk should contain all the necessary minerals (calcium, phosphorus, magnesium, sodium, chlorine, potassium), trace elements (iron, copper, zinc, iodine, selenium, fluorine, manganese), and vitamins (A, D3, E, K, C, B-group vitamins), as well as a certain number of essential amino acids (such as tryptophan and arginine), without forgetting the essential fatty acids (linoleic, linolenic, and arachidonic acids). Finally, kittens, like adult cats, require taurine in the diet.

• Dilution of the milk. The dilution recommended by the manufacturer must be considered in conjunction with the indicated composition. Substitute mother's milk is generally sold as a powder that must be mixed with water. Depending on the product, it is recommended that one part powder be diluted in two or three parts water.

EXAMPLE OF HOMEMADE MILK REPLACER FOR KITTENS

(Meyer, 1989 from Hall, 1992).

Cow's milk, skim (ml)	600
Low-fat fromage blanc (g)	190
Lean ground beef (5% fat) (g)	90
Soybean oil (g)	30
Egg yolk (g)	20
Mineral and vitamin supplement (g)	10

• Ease of administering, cleaning, etc. Usually, manufacturers supply bottles with nipples more or less adapted for kittens.

• The results obtained. This is by far the most important criteria. Kittens must grow (gain weight) steadily without diarrhea, etc.

Hygiene and Feeding Schedule

The method used for bottle feeding is at least as important as the quality of the milk administered. The feeding schedule must be regular over 24 hours, both day and night, with feeding occurring more frequently the younger the kitten: from seven bottles every 24 hours in the first week to two in the sixth week, with solid food being offered by the time the kitten is thirty days old. Strict hygiene must be observed during feedings, as kittens are fragile and must be protected from infection:

• The person who prepares the milk and administers the bottles must be sure to wash his or her hands prior to these activities;

• Before the bottles are filled with milk, they must be thoroughly cleaned (with a bottle brush) and rinsed in very hot water. They must also be sterilized regularly;

• The milk must be prepared just prior to feeding;

• Unless the manufacturer indicates otherwise, the milk must be prepared using water that has been boiled and cooled to a temperature of 37 to 38°C before feeding;

• At each bottle feeding, the kitten must be allowed to suckle freely;

• When the kittens are young, the caregiver should stimulate their perineum with a warm, damp cloth during suckling to imitate the mother's licking behavior and thereby stimulate urination and defecation.

Weaning

Weaning is the change from a milk diet to a solid diet. Weaning is a physiological necessity, for both the kitten and the mother. The kitten's nutritional requirements increase steadily, while lactation begins to decline around five or six weeks after birth. A milk diet thus becomes insufficient to fulfill the litter's dietary requirements. At the same time, the kitten develops, its digestive capacities increase, and its body becomes ready for a solid diet.

By four to five weeks old, the kitten may start to show interest in its mother's food, at first licking the food around its mother's mouth. So as to be accessible to kittens, the food dish must be wide and have fairly low edges. In addition, in the case of dry food, the pieces must be small enough for kittens to pick up. With a specially adapted diet, it is best if the food given to the mother during lactation is the same as the food the kittens will be given after weaning. This helps prevent adding the stress of dietary change to that of weaning.

The time of weaning is based on a number of criteria, some of which are contradictory: For the mother, especially in the case of large litters, weaning fairly early prevents too many of her dietary reserves from being depleted. For kittens, weaning is highly stressful (change in type of diet, separation from the mother's nest) and need not be early, to the extent that a sufficient quantity of milk is available.

In practice, weaning can begin when the kittens' growth rate decreases. The kittens' consumption of solid food must be monitored and should increase steadily starting when they are four weeks old. Kittens can be weaned when they consume approximately 20 g of dry matter per day, or approximately 25 g of dry food or 70 g of canned food, generally when they are around six to seven weeks old.

For kittens raised on a bottle with a milk replacer, the number of daily feedings should be reduced in the week preceding the chosen weaning period (for example, going from four to three bottles per day) and, after each feeding, the kittens should be offered a bowl of solid food moistened with the substitute mother's milk. During the week chosen for weaning (when the kittens are around five weeks old), the kittens should be offered the solid food before bottle feeding. One or two bottles per day may still be necessary, depending on the kitten. The kitten's weight is the golden rule—it must increase steadily. The kittens must be weighed in the morning, prior to the first meal. Gradually, the amount of food made available between meals should be increased, first as a soupy mixture, then as solid food soaked with less and less milk, then with the milk gradually being replaced by water. By the end of the week, the solid food should be moistened with water alone.

Even though weaning should occur gradually, the weaning period must not be too long. The kittens should be prepared for weaning starting at four to five weeks old, and weaning should be complete by the time they are seven weeks old. This will allow the mother to recover from this period of great stress on her body.

Very early weaning (at four to five weeks old) is necessary under some circumstances (orphaned kittens, feline infectious peritonitis, etc.). If early weaning is done properly and the kittens are fed carefully, the stronger kittens will be affected very little. However, morbidity (the number of sick kittens) may increase in the weaker kittens, especially in the case of underfeeding.

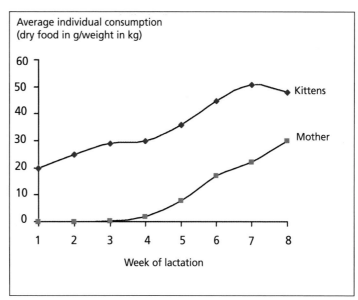

AVERAGE DIETARY CONSUMPTION OF THE MOTHER CAT AND HER KITTENS

(average of three kittens per litter) (dry food in g/weight in kg, with dry food at 4.5 kcal/g)

(from Legrand-Defretin and Munday, 1995).

Weaning is a necessary evil in the lifecycle. It is a required step toward independence but also a highly stressful period for kittens. Weaning must therefore be carried out with utmost care.

Adulthood

Cats spend approximately one-third their time sleeping and one-third playing, with the last third divided between eating and grooming.

When a cat has free access to the outdoors, it will willingly hunt small prey (mice, young birds, small birds) that it may or may not eat, when it is fed elsewhere. Even if it does not have access to the outdoors, a domestic cat will still exhibit this predatory behavior. Indeed, all cats are drawn to moving objects and can spend hours kicking a ball around.

A cat that eats only mice must consume eight to ten mice per day to fulfill its dietary requirements. Hunting mice is not easy, and just spotting one is not enough to catch it. Hunting is very time-consuming, and failure is frequent. Still, cats do have terrific assets for hunting and catching prey. They have keen senses of hearing, sight, and smell, mobile whiskers, sharp claws, great nimbleness, and one particularly special skill—the ability to move without making a sound.

Normal weaning							
Weeks	1	2	3	4	5	6	7
Number of bottles/day	7	6	5	5	4	2	
Solid food					+	++	+++
Early weaning							
Days	1-7	8-14	15-21	22-28	29-31	32-35	36-42	43-49
Number of bottles/day	7	6	5	3	3			
Solid food					+	++	+++	+++

For example, six bottles per 24-hour day means one bottle every 24/6 = four hours, including at night.

SAMPLE FEEDING SCHEDULES FOR MILK REPLACER.

(adapted from Campanac, 1985).

The Claws and Teeth

A cat's claws have several special features: They grow constantly throughout the cat's life, are slightly curved, and are sharp and retractile, being attached vertically.

A cat's ability to extend its claws has several consequences. First, with its claws retracted, the cat can move silently, thanks to its delicate paw pads. Next, cats can retract their claws to protect them, as they are valuable hunting and fighting weapons. Finally, when the claws are extended, they serve both as fearsome sharp, slicing weapons and as a precious tool for climbing trees.

Thanks to the shape of its claws, a cat can easily sink them into its prey or enemies, like a set of tiny knives. Clawing, even in play, always leaves at least a nice scratch on the skin.

It is entirely possible for owners to clip their cat's claws, but several precautions must be taken. First, owners must use a specially adapted nail clipper that is in good condition. Next, the cat must be held firmly, so that the paw does not slip when the nail is clipped. Finally, once the owner is well-equipped and well-positioned, he or she must take the end of the cat's foot, lightly squeeze the tip of the toe between two fingers, and cut in the direction of the claw (unlike when clipping human nails) to avoid crushing it. When a claw is extended in this manner, two areas become apparent: a pinkish area near the toe and a lighter area near the tip. The light area is what must be cut, as the pinkish area is the nail root and contains blood vessels. The cat is equipped with four claws on each hind foot and five on each forefoot. The fifth of these front claws is called the dew claw (it is located on the toe corresponding to our thumb). This claw must be monitored, since if it is not clipped, it could curl around into the skin and injure the paw. Many cats willingly use tree trunks or, when unavailable, a vertical plank as a scratching post. Scratching serves to file the nails, not so much to wear them down as to renew them, as scratching removes the old outer layer of the claw to expose the underlying sharper claw. Some cats will actually clip their nails on their own—you may see them chewing on a nail as if to bite it off.

After its claws, a cat's teeth are its second line of natural defense, especially its fangs. A cat's teeth are better adapted to seizing, shredding, and tearing prey than to chewing food, which is often swallowed whole.

Water

Some cats may be good swimmers, but they are fairly rare. Cats' general aversion to water is evident in their behavior while drinking. Cats probably originated in the desert and drink very little. Their urine is highly concentrated. Cats that consume prey also drink water, but not as much, since 60% of the prey's body is water, whether it is a mouse or a bird. Similarly, cats that eat wet food from a can tend to drink very little or not at all, while those that eat dry food drink in addition to eating. Cats will consume water in small quantities, drinking from ten to twenty times per day. It is therefore essential that cats have access to clean water at all times. The belief that dry food promotes disease, kidney-related disease in particular, is absolutely false. Still, it is essential to make sure that the cat drinks enough water for proper kidney functioning.

Spaying and Neutering

Approximately 50% of domestic cats, both male and female, are altered. Altering poses no particular problems, except with regard to diet, since the change in status causes an increase in appetite and a decrease in caloric requirements, both in males and females. Consequently, altered cats should either be given less food or a food lower in calories to prevent them from becoming overweight. Owners can even accustom their cat to receiving less food one to two weeks before the scheduled operation. Thus accustomed, the cat will adapt even more easily to its new status.

Life Expectancy

Although some cats reach the record age of 30 years old, a cat's average life expectancy is ten years for altered cats. In whole cats, life expectancy decreases to six years for females and five years for males. This difference can be explained by the tendency of whole cats to stray and therefore be more exposed to risks including both traffic and contagious disease, infections, parasites, etc. Indeed, whenever cats have access to the outdoors, they tend to come into contact with other cats either to reproduce or to fight for territory or mates. These close encounters promote the spread of disease and ultimately shorten the cat's life. Still, the number of elderly cats continues to rise, indicating a better adapted diet, vaccinations that are more common and more effective, and improved medical care.

Old Age

The number of elderly cats in the feline population continues to grow. Of the 8.2 million cats in France, slightly more than 30% are over 8 years old, and 900,000 (11% of France's total feline population) are over 11 years old. Just like in humans, old age is a separate stage in a cat's life. Aging is a natural, unavoidable phenomenon in cats as in other species. It appears in a number of ways: decreased energy, a tendency toward lethargy, difficulty walking, lack of appetite, and a greater frequency of various illnesses including cardiac problems (ventricular hypertrophy), particularly due to the decreased elasticity of the arterial walls, respiratory difficulties due to the decline in pulmonary functioning, susceptibility to infection

due to a weakened immune system, frequent kidney disease, tumors, and endocrine problems such as hyperthyroidism, diabetes, etc.

The majority of overweight cats are between 6 and 10 years old, with older cats tending instead to be thin. Obesity is a risk factor in a large number of diseases, such as diabetes, skin problems, etc., but thinness should not be favored for this reason. Indeed, a cat that does not consume enough calories will lose weight, but if the cat does not consume enough protein, it will lose muscle, and its immune system will become weaker.

A cat's appetite may decrease with age, both because of frequent mouth problems (gingivitis, ulcers, tumors) and because of a decline in digestive capacities. The quality and quantity of the diet should therefore be monitored for cats over 10 years old. Elderly cats tend also to drink less and can quickly become dehydrated, so the amount of water in their diet and their water consumption must be monitored as well. In addition, many illnesses occur more often in elderly cats than in young cats. For example, kidney failure is more common in older cats, in part because of the slow onset of this illness. Elderly cats should be monitored by a veterinarian so that any illness can be treated as soon as possible. One veterinary examination per year is recommended throughout a cat's life, for example at the time of vaccination. One examination every six months is strongly advised for cats over 12 years old.

From birth to old age, the cat is primarily a carnivore and a hunter, independent and proud. From a very early age, cats are drawn to moving objects. As adults, they love petting just as much as roaming in the great outdoors. Whatever the breed, and at all stages of life, cats are fascinating animals to observe and live with.

Elderly cat walking through a meadow.

Genetics

Each individual is characterized by a multitude of traits which, taken as a whole, form what is known in genetics as the phenotype. In cats, these traits involve morphology (size, shape of the head and body, eye shape, etc.) and coloring (of the coat and eyes), as well as physiological (frequency of heats, average litter size) and psychological aspects.

All these traits are determined by proteins which are either structural proteins or enzymes. Each protein is manufactured by the cells in an organism, thanks to a gene. All the genes are contained in the nucleus of each cell as long chains of DNA (deoxyribonucleic acid) that form the chromosomes.

In each cell of the so-called "higher" life forms, including the cat, all chromosomes—and therefore all genes—exist in duplicate. Cats have nineteen pairs of identical chromosomes, for a total of thirty-eight chromosomes. Actually, this is completely true only of female cats, since one pair of chromosomes—the sex-determining chromosomes—is special. Female

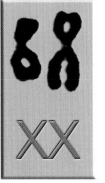

Female

Male

cats have two identical X chromosomes, whereas males have two different sex-determining chromosomes: one X chromosome and one Y chromosome. It is the Y chromosome that causes an embryo to develop as a male.

At puberty, a cat's body manufactures reproductive cells, or gametes (eggs in the female and sperm in the male). Unlike other cells, the gametes contain only one copy of each pair of chromosomes, or one copy of each of the genes that the parent carries in duplicate. In fertilization, the sperm and egg unite to produce one cell, the future kitten, that now contains a full thirty-eight chromosomes: nineteen from the mother and nineteen from the father. In this way, parents transmit half their gene pool to their offspring. The offspring will have a phenotype resulting from the combination of all the genes provided by the two parents, and thus a certain resemblance to their parents.

One of the pleasures and objectives of pure-bred cat breeders is to improve the genetic makeup of their animals.
To this end, breeders must determine which genes are carried by all individuals of a given breed and choose for reproduction the individuals with the most interesting genes. This

process is known as selection. Next, the breeder crosses individuals that complement each other in terms of the genes they carry, in order to obtain offspring that improve upon the aesthetic qualities of the breed. This is known as logical mating. The science that makes this possible is called genetics.

Now, let us look at how breeders work and how genetics works. We have chosen to present these topics in an extremely simplified manner that will be easy for everyone to understand:

• We will confine ourselves to the genes that determine hair length and coat color;

• We will turn the genetics of feline coat color into a card game!

Readers who wish to see how the terms used here correspond to the terms used in genetics may refer to the following table.

How Sex is Determined

As an introduction to how the card game works, let us apply this analogy to the determination of sex in kittens. In each cell of her body, the female cat holds two X cards (with an X chromosome), so each of the eggs her body manufactures will contain one of these two X cards. In each of his cells, the male cat holds one X card and one Y card. He will therefore produce sperm containing either an X card or a Y card. During fertilization, either the egg encounters a sperm with an X card, and the kitten will be female, or the egg encounters a sperm with a Y card, and the kitten will be male. The Punnet square is a simple representation of all the possible crosses between sperm and egg. It indicates that ultimately, half the offspring will be female and half will be male.

EXACT TERMS IN GENETICS

Element of the Card Game	Corresponding Term in Genetics
A series of cards	A locus
One card in a series	An allelic gene (or simply an allele)
A strong card	A dominant allele
A weak card	A recessive allele
Two cards of equal strength	Two co-dominant alleles
The card in a series that is most common in cats	The wild-type allele
The card(s) in a series that are fairly rare in cats	The mutant-type allele(s)
The combination of all cards held by a cat	The cat's genotype

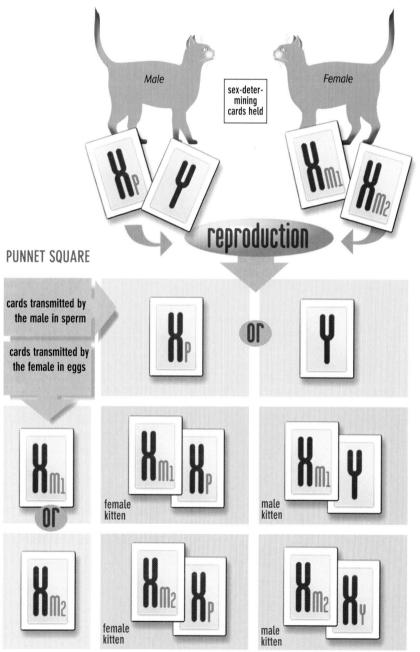

P = paternal   M = maternal

81

The Card Game and Coat Color

Now let us apply the card game to coat color and hair length in cats. Based on current knowledge in genetics, this game would include twenty-five cards arranged in eleven series.
- eight series of two cards each (A, B, Ch, D, I, L, S, and W series)
- three series of three cards each (C, T, and O series)

The Card Game of Coat Color and Hair Length in Cats

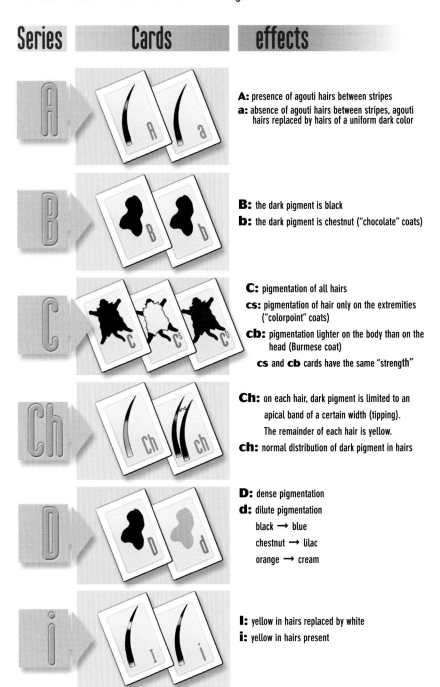

Series	Cards	effects
A		**A:** presence of agouti hairs between stripes **a:** absence of agouti hairs between stripes, agouti hairs replaced by hairs of a uniform dark color
B		**B:** the dark pigment is black **b:** the dark pigment is chestnut ("chocolate" coats)
C		**C:** pigmentation of all hairs **cs:** pigmentation of hair only on the extremities ("colorpoint" coats) **cb:** pigmentation lighter on the body than on the head (Burmese coat) **cs** and **cb** cards have the same "strength"
Ch		**Ch:** on each hair, dark pigment is limited to an apical band of a certain width (tipping). The remainder of each hair is yellow. **ch:** normal distribution of dark pigment in hairs
D		**D:** dense pigmentation **d:** dilute pigmentation black → blue chestnut → lilac orange → cream
i		**I:** yellow in hairs replaced by white **i:** yellow in hairs present

82

Note that the O series is a bit special, since it is located on the sex-determining X chromosome. Thus, this series contains the following cards: XO, Xo, and Y. Similarly, the combined effects of the A and T series require some explanation; see the illustrations on the next page.

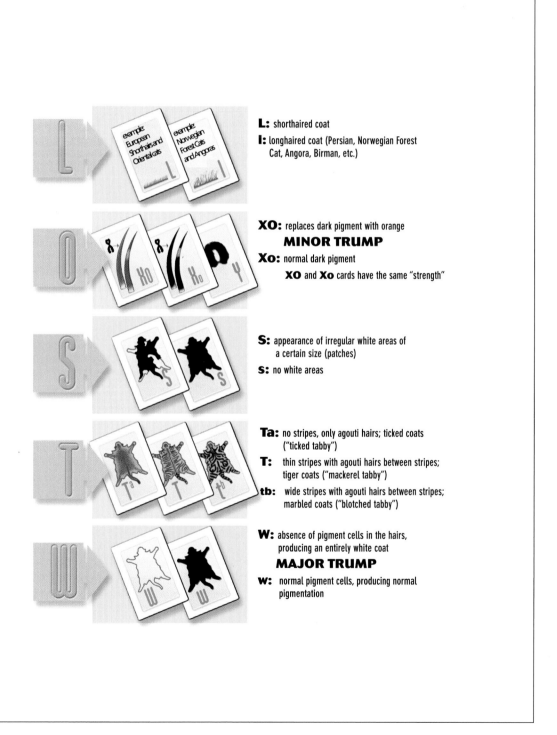

L: shorthaired coat

l: longhaired coat (Persian, Norwegian Forest Cat, Angora, Birman, etc.)

XO: replaces dark pigment with orange
MINOR TRUMP
Xo: normal dark pigment

XO and **Xo** cards have the same "strength"

S: appearance of irregular white areas of a certain size (patches)

s: no white areas

Ta: no stripes, only agouti hairs; ticked coats ("ticked tabby")

T: thin stripes with agouti hairs between stripes; tiger coats ("mackerel tabby")

tb: wide stripes with agouti hairs between stripes; marbled coats ("blotched tabby")

W: absence of pigment cells in the hairs, producing an entirely white coat
MAJOR TRUMP
w: normal pigment cells, producing normal pigmentation

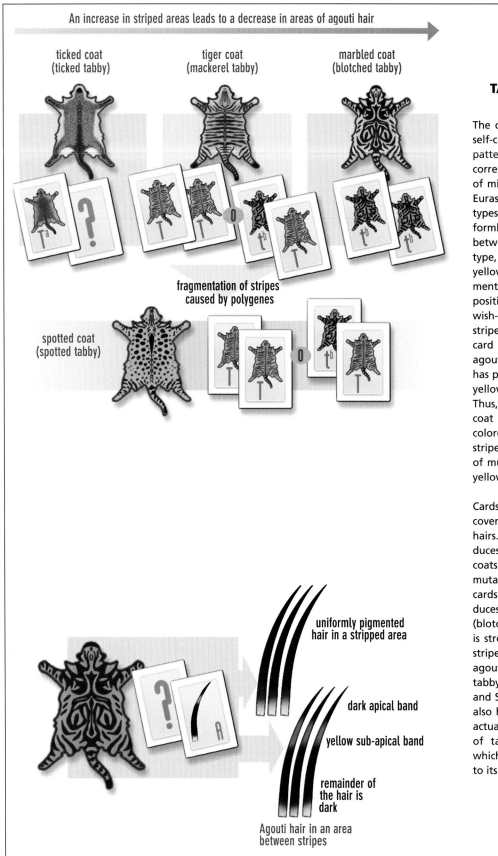

An increase in striped areas leads to a decrease in areas of agouti hair

ticked coat
(ticked tabby)

tiger coat
(mackerel tabby)

marbled coat
(blotched tabby)

fragmentation of stripes
caused by polygenes

spotted coat
(spotted tabby)

uniformly pigmented
hair in a stripped area

dark apical band

yellow sub-apical band

remainder of
the hair is
dark

Agouti hair in an area
between stripes

TABBY AND SELF VARIETIES

The cards in the A and T series determine self-colored coats and the various striped patterns known as tabby coats. Tabby coats correspond to the most common phenotype of mixed breed cats, as well as that of the Eurasian wild cat. Tabby coats contain two types of hair. The hair in the stripes is uniformly colored by dark pigment. The hairs between the stripes are of the "agouti" type, that is, they have a sub-apical band of yellow pigment that interrupts the dark pigment; breeders call this "ticking." The juxtaposition of agouti hairs produces the yellowish-chestnut coloring of areas between stripes that is typical of tabby cats. The A card is what determines the existence of agouti hairs. A mutation in the domestic cat has produced a weak a card that erases the yellow sub-apical band on agouti hairs. Thus, a self-colored black cat actually has a coat consisting of black stripes (uniformly colored "normal" hairs) and areas between stripes that are also black, since they consist of mutant agouti hairs that have lost their yellow band.

Cards in the T series define the shape and coverage of stripes with relation to agouti hairs. The T card, considered "wild," produces the thin striping of so-called tiger coats (mackerel tabby for the British). Two mutations have produced two new T series cards. One, the tb card, is weak and produces the wide stripes of marbled coats (blotched tabby). The other mutant card, Ta, is stronger than the T card and erases the stripes. The resulting coat contains only agouti hairs and is called "ticked" (ticked tabby). This coat is found in the Abyssinian and Singapura. Note that a self-colored cat also holds T cards. This means that its coat actually has one of the three possible types of tabby markings, but we cannot tell which, except by observing what it transmits to its offspring.

What are the ground rules of the feline coat color game?

1 – Each cell in a cat's body holds two cards from each series.

2 – To make a gamete, take one card at random from each series in the parent's set of cards.

3 – To make a kitten, randomly select one set of cards for the sperm from among all the sets potentially produced by the male, and combine them with one set of cards for the egg from among all the sets potentially produced by the female. These random combinations are represented in a Punnet square.

4 – In some series, the cards have different "strengths." Place the stronger card on top of the weaker card. The names of stronger cards are in uppercase letters, and the names of weaker cards are in lowercase letters. For example, in the L series, the cat will have short hair if it holds two L cards or one L card and one l card. In the latter case, the stronger L card imposes its effect. The cat will have long hair only if it holds two weak l cards.

In other series, all the cards are equal in strength. The combination of two equal cards produces an effect that is intermediate to the effect of each card taken separately. For example, in the O series, the XO card produces orange pigmentation, while the Xo card produces non-orange pigmentation. The combination XO Xo produces a coat with a juxtaposition of patches of orange hairs and patches of non-orange hairs. This is what breeders call a "tortoiseshell" coat (see Part 1, Section 3). Similarly, in the C series, the combination of a cs card and a cb card produces a special coat corresponding to that of the Tonkinese breed.

5 – Finally, as in many card games, there are trump cards, or cards that are stronger than those in other series. In our game, the O series acts like a minor trump. The XO card in this

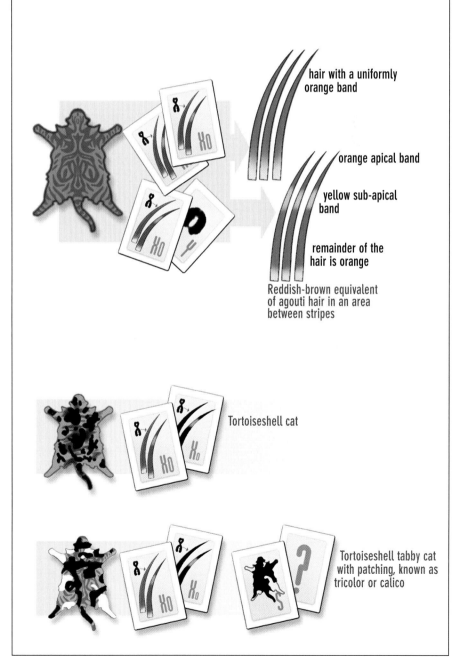

REDDISH BROWN CATS AND TORTOISESHELL CATS

A very special mutation in cats has produced an O card for a gene located on the sex-determining X chromosome. The O card turns all the dark pigment in the hair into an intense orange pigment. Thus, a reddish-brown tabby cat has a coat consisting on the one hand of stripes of entirely orange hairs (the equivalent of uniformly dark-colored hairs in tabby cats that are not reddish-brown), and on the other hand of areas between stripes consisting of orange hairs with a yellow sub-apical band (the equivalent of agouti hairs). This reddish-brown coat is exclusive to XOY males and XOXO females. Females with XOXo cards have a special coat pattern called tortoiseshell tabby (tortie tabby for the British). This coat is a mosaic of patches of the reddish-brown tabby cat type and patches of the "normal" tabby cat type. If the female also holds the S card that produces white patches, then the coat is called tricolor or calico.

hair with a uniformly orange band

orange apical band

yellow sub-apical band

remainder of the hair is orange

Reddish-brown equivalent of agouti hair in an area between stripes

Tortoiseshell cat

Tortoiseshell tabby cat with patching, known as tricolor or calico

series produces orange pigmentation that masks the effect of B series cards. In the W series, the W card is a major trump, since it masks the effects of all the cards in other series except those in the L series.

This major trump card status is easy to understand, to the extent that since the W card erases melanocytes (the cells that synthesize pigment), a cat that holds a W card will be all white due to the absence of pigment. None of the effects of the other cards acting on pigment are visible, given the lack of pigment.

How can you tell which cards potential parents hold?

We will use three examples to illustrate this technique.

Example 1:
The cat's phenotype is solid blue with short hair. For all traits determined by weak cards, the cat must hold two weak cards. Thus, in this case, we can predict that this cat must hold two a cards (since it has no agouti hairs and therefore solid coloring), two ch cards, and two i cards (since the hairs have no tipping or partial decoloration), two d cards (because blue is a dilution of black), two s cards (since there are no white patches), and

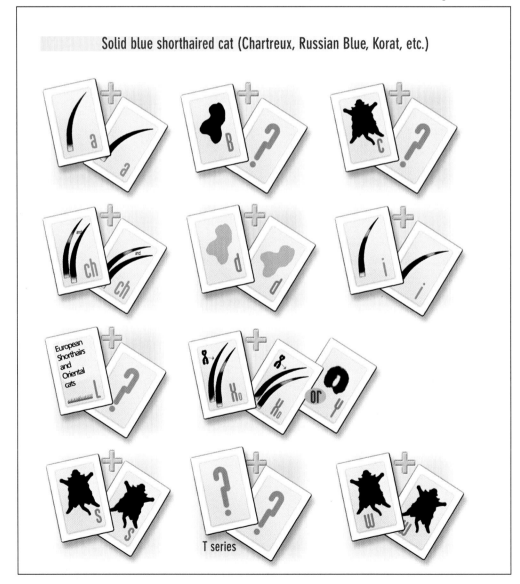

Solid blue shorthaired cat (Chartreux, Russian Blue, Korat, etc.)

T series

86

two w cards (since melanocytes are present). In terms of the O series, if the cat is male, it must hold one Y card and one Xo card (since it is not reddish-brown), and if it is female, it must hold two Xo cards (since it is neither reddish-brown nor tortoiseshell). For traits determined by strong cards, the cat must hold at least one corresponding strong card, with the other card in the series being unknown, either strong or weak. The cat in our example thus holds at least one L card (since it has short hair), one B card (since its basic pigment is black and not chestnut), and one C card (since it is neither colorpoint nor shaded like a Burmese). Finally, we cannot tell which T series cards the cat holds, since the striped markings are not visible. The various unknowns cannot be ascertained without additional information on the coat color of the cat's parents and/or offspring.

Example 2:
The animal is longhaired, with tortoiseshell and blotched tabby markings (dark stripes are present). Using the same reasoning as above, we can predict that this cat must hold two i, ch, l, s, tb (since the stripes are wide), and w cards. It must also hold at least one A, B, C, and D card. Finally, since it is a tortoiseshell, it must hold one XO card and one Xo card. In passing, we know that this type of coat is specific to females.

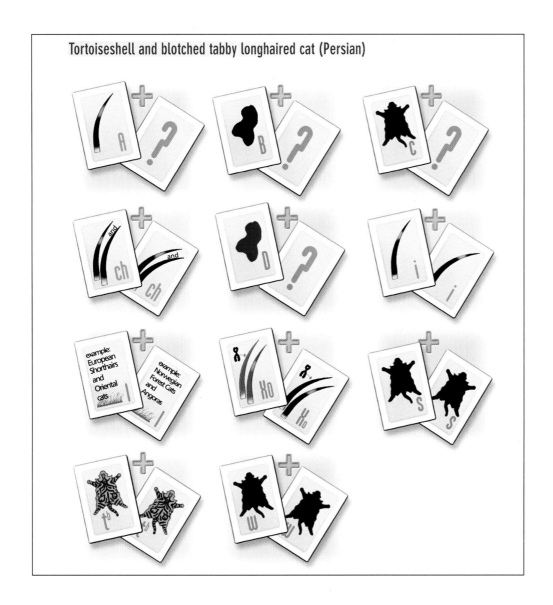

Tortoiseshell and blotched tabby longhaired cat (Persian)

Example 3:

The final example is a shorthaired variety of cat called a "silver blotched tabby." We can tell it is different from the traditional striped cat because the areas between the stripes are light-colored and silvery in appearance, rather than brownish-yellow.

This is because the agouti hairs between the stripes have undergone a partial decoloration affecting the yellow sub-apical band. From this we can deduce that this cat holds at least one strong I card.

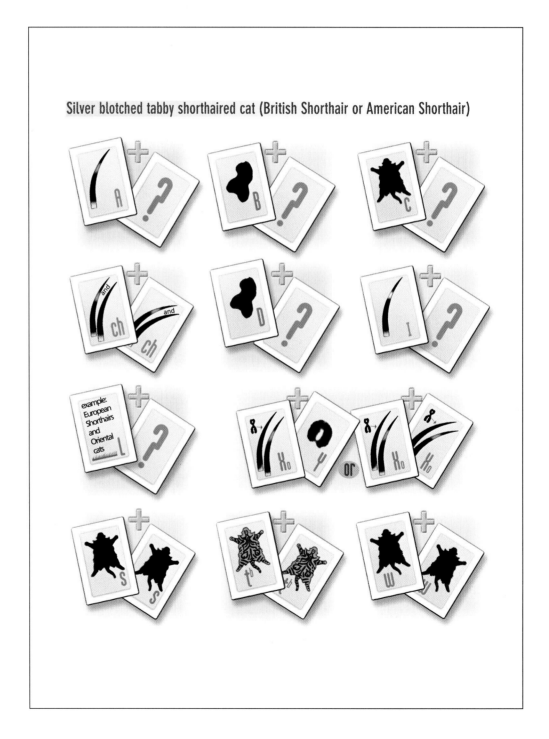

Silver blotched tabby shorthaired cat (British Shorthair or American Shorthair)

How can we predict what types of kittens will be produced from crosses between known parents?

Case 1: What types of kittens will be produced by crossing a reddish-brown tom with a tortoiseshell queen?

To simplify the game and our predictions, it is important that we limit the question to the series of cards that are interesting in this case.

Here, what interests us most are the O series cards held by each parent. These cards are XO and Y for the father, and XO and Xo for the mother. The sperm produced by the father will have either an XO card or a Y card. The eggs produced by the mother will have either an XO card or an Xo card. The various kittens that will result from the random combination of these eggs and sperm appear in the Punnet square below. Note that if a sufficient number of kittens are produced, half of them will be

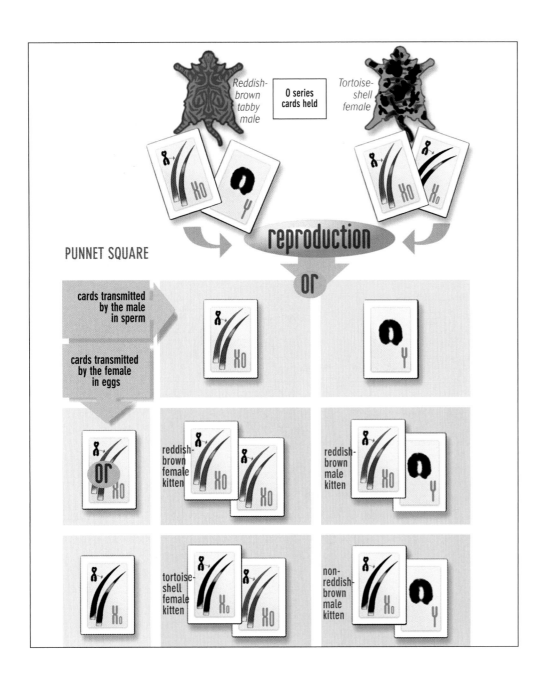

reddish-brown (male and female), one-fourth will be non-reddish-brown males (either tabby or self-colored, depending on the parents' cards in the other series), and one-fourth will be tortoiseshell females. This cross will therefore produce quite a range of offspring!

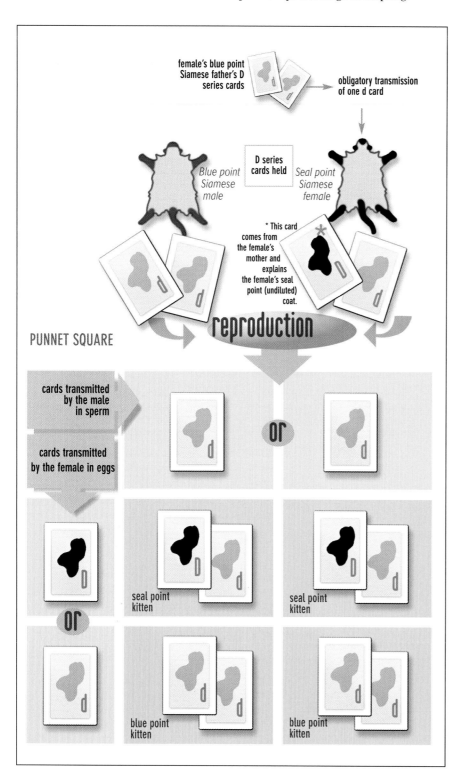

female's blue point Siamese father's D series cards

obligatory transmission of one d card

D series cards held

Blue point Siamese male

Seal point Siamese female

* This card comes from the female's mother and explains the female's seal point (undiluted) coat.

reproduction

PUNNET SQUARE

cards transmitted by the male in sperm

cards transmitted by the female in eggs

or

seal point kitten

seal point kitten

or

blue point kitten

blue point kitten

Case 2: What would be the result of crossing two Siamese cats: a blue point tom and a seal point queen from a blue point father? In this case, we do not consider the C series, since both parents are Siamese. The Siamese (colorpoint) pattern is determined by the weak cs card, so each parent must hold two cs cards and can therefore transmit only cs cards to its offspring. In other words, all the kittens will be Siamese.

However, the D series is very interesting. The blue coloring of the blue point variety is a dilution of black pigment, and the dilution card d is a weak card. Thus, the tom must hold two d cards. As for the queen, she is black in appearance (or "seal point," to use the accepted term), so she must hold at least one D card (since dilution is absent). However, since her father was blue point and therefore held two d cards, he must have transmitted one d card to her. Thus, we know exactly which two D series cards the queen in this cross must hold. She is said to be a "carrier" of dilution.

The Punnet square reveals the various types of kittens we would obtain: 50% seal point Siamese kittens (with black extremities) and 50% blue point Siamese kittens (with blue extremities).

Both a Conclusion and an Introduction

This brief overview of feline genetics is enough to show how breeders can select (choose) the parents they find interesting in terms of appearance (coat color and hair length) and then cross them in a logical manner to obtain kittens of the varieties they desire.

The breeder might focus on maintaining the range of coat colors that is traditional in a particular breed. But the breeder can also use these techniques to introduce a new coat color that did not exist previously in a breed. For example, beginning in the 1930s, breeders launched breeding programs aimed at introducing the cs card into the Persian breed. The Siamese cat provided this cs card. After extensive efforts focused on recovering the typical Persian morphology, which was significantly modified by the Siamese morphology genes transmitted with the cs card, breeders arrived at the magnificent colorpoint Persians we can now admire in cat shows.

This same technique is used to create new breeds from a spontaneous mutation. A spontaneous mutation is actually a new card that appears in the game. For example, in 1981 a female cat with ears curled back over the head was discovered in the United States. This was a spontaneous mutation determined by a strong card.

In this manner, a new series of cards was added to the game: the Cu series determining ear curl. This series includes a weak cu card that determines "normal" ears and a strong Cu card that determines the new, curled type of ears. Next, through selection and logical mating, breeders produced enough cats with the Cu card that a new breed of cat, the American Curl, was recognized.

Not all spontaneous mutations are harmless to a cat's health. Some cause hereditary genetic diseases. In this case, breeding is aimed at

---

PRIMARY CONGENITAL AND HEREDITARY CONDITIONS DESCRIBED IN PUREBRED CATS
(modified based on Ph. Bossé, 1994)

Breed	Affected functions or organs	Affections
Abyssinian	Kidneys	Renal amyloidosis
	Eyes	Retinal atrophy
	Nervous system	Lysosomal accumulation neuropathy
	Thyroid	Hypothyroidism
Burmese	Skeleton	Craniofacial deformities, dorsoventral flattening
	Muscles	Periodic muscle weakness
Korat	Nervous system	Lysosomal accumulation neuropathy
Manx	Vertebral skeleton	Sacrococcygeal hyopoplasia, spina bifida, incontinence, locomotor ailments
Persian	Kidneys	Polycystic kidney
	Eyes	Corneal sequestration, photophobia, hypopigmentation, cataracts
	Nervous system	Lysosomal accumulation neuropathy
	Abdomen	Peritoneopericardial defect
Cornish Rex	Abdomen	Umbilical hernia
	Thymus (?)	Wasting syndrome
Devon Rex	Skeleton	Patellar luxation
	Coagulation	Hemorrhagic ailments
	Muscles	Respiratory muscle degeneration
Scottish Fold	Skeleton	Limb and tail defects
Siamese	Skeleton	Craniofacial defects (hydrocephalus, cleft palate), knotted tail
	Nervous system	Lysosomal accumulation neuropathy
	Eyes	Retinal degeneration, strabismus
	Skin	Hypotrichosis

identifying the individuals that carry bad cards and not using them to renew the breed.

To conclude, we must mention that the simple reasoning presented here applies only to traits determined by single genes with a significant effect, or major genes. This is the case for the majority of coat color traits and for a certain number of specific morphological traits (absence of tail, folded ears, short legs, etc.). This is not true for so-called quantitative traits that affect morphology, physiology, and psychology. The current view is that these traits are produced by a combination of many polygenes, or genes that each have a very slight effect. Selective breeding based on polygenic traits is more delicate and complex than that based on traits determined by a single gene. This is why we did not broach the subject in this short presentation. Still, this concept is extremely important in establishing and maintaining many of the features that characterize each feline breed and are recorded in its respective standard. Note that some pigmentation traits, although determined essentially by the major genes described above, are also influenced by polygenes. This is true of irregular white spots (or patches), in particular. This explains why breeders have such difficulty establishing these traits definitively.

COATS WITH WHITE PATCHES

In cats, the irregular white spots called patches are determined by a mutation that has produced a strong card S. However, the extent of white patches is significantly modified by a whole set of polygenes, or genes that each have a slight effect individually. Of course, all intermediate forms (including harlequin and bicolor van varieties) are based on the polygenes carried by each individual. It is very difficult, even impossible, to establish a breed with a specific pattern of white patches. This is true especially of the Birman, whose famous white-gloved paws are actually minimal patches that vary from one animal to the next, based on polygenes. To make matters worse, a "well-gloved" cat will not necessarily produce offspring that are all well-gloved.

Let us mention in passing that the Birman also holds two cs cards that superimpose a colorpoint coat on its glove markings.

Preventive Medicine

Parasites and External Fungi

There are many and varied parasites and fungi responsible for skin disorders in cats. Mites are microscopic animals responsible for mange or itching. Insects such as fleas and lice can be found in a cat's coat. They cause conditions called respectively pulicosis (flea infestation) and pediculosis (louse infestation).

Dermatophytes are microscopic filamentous fungi that subsist on the keratin in hair or on the surface of the skin. They are the agents responsible for ringworm.

Some of the pathogenic agents described here can be transmitted to humans. Cheyletiella mites produce a small scabby rash on the body and pruritis (itching). Itching may be so intense that a visit to a dermatologist is necessary. In this case, based on the lesions, the physician may recommend that the owner take his cat to a veterinarian to treat the cat for parasites.

Fleas found on domestic animals occasionally get the taste for human blood. Finally, dermatophytes, particularly the species common to cats, are easily transmitted to humans. They produce annular lesions, called tinea circinata, on glabrous (smooth and bare) skin, most often on the forearms, face, or neck. Unlike the symptoms observed in the animal, inflammation and itching in humans can be extreme.

Of all feline skin disorders, pulicosis (flea infestation) and ringworm merit particular attention. These disorders are very common and often difficult or impossible to prevent, particularly when we consider that the cat is not an isolated animal, but part of a community of cats.

Flea Infestation (Pulicosis)

Ctenocephalides felis (cat flea) is not finicky. This flea will feed on a wide variety of mammals, including cats, dogs, herbivores, and humans. Many cats are not sensitive to flea bites. However, some cats develop allergic reactions to flea bites and the symptoms of dermatitis appear as a result. This allergic reaction presents in the form of miliary dermatitis, a red, crusty rash on the back and around the neck. The skin takes on a sandy appearance. Since the infected animal scratches incessantly, there is a danger that it might scratch and injure itself.

Some animals respond to the irritation caused by the fleas by constantly cleaning and licking themselves. This may result in hairloss on the abdomen, thighs, flanks, or tail. Fleas also carry diseases. They transmit tapeworms and the bacteria responsible for cat-scratch disease.

Research carried out over the last decade studying the biology of cat fleas has given us insight into their life cycle. Full understanding

Microscopic ear mites (Otodectes cynotis) responsible for otitis externa in carnivores

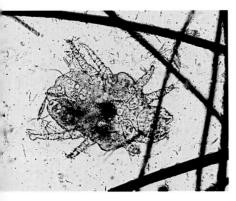

Microscopic mites (Cheyletiella blakei) responsible for cheyletiellosis in cats

of this life cycle is required if we are to effectively prevent infestation.

We now know that there are a number of misconceptions regarding cat fleas. The first is that adult fleas do not remain on the cat, but only stop in for a meal. In fact, adult fleas spend their entire life on the same animal. Only a very small number of fleas on a cat will move to other nearby domestic animals. Therefore, the risk of contamination from other animals in the veterinarian's waiting room or at a cat show is almost zero.

Adult fleas reproduce rapidly. Each female is capable of laying up to fifty eggs per day for a period of several weeks. These white, ovoid eggs are 0.5 mm long. They do not attach to the animal, and therefore fall to the floor as the animal moves about. Under favorable temperature and humidity conditions, the eggs hatch in several days, revealing wormlike larvae several millimeters in length. These larvae are not parasites.

They feed on the organic debris found in their surroundings, particularly adult flea feces. Larvae love humidity, but dislike light. At the end of the larval stage (a few days to one month), each larva weaves a cocoon around itself. Adult fleas emerge a few days later, bringing the metamorphosis cycle to a close. If conditions are favorable (if animals are present in the environment), the adult emerges immediately. If no animals are present, the adult fleas are able to survive in their cocoon for several months.

The adult fleas that remain in the cocoon will immediately take advantage of a host if it passes by. Fleas that are still in their protective cocoon are relatively unaffected by insecticides. Once they emerge, the adult fleas actively search for a host.

In conclusion, it is important to remember that adult fleas are parasites, but in their immature forms, they live freely in the environment. The life cycle of fleas is very short

(three weeks is often sufficient). Recently emerged fleas pose the greatest risk, not fleas already happily inhabiting another host.

Eliminating Fleas

Effective control requires treating fleas on the body of the cat as well as the physical surroundings. Products used to prevent flea infestation must meet two criteria: They must take effect immediately and be long-acting (residual activity). Fleas must be eliminated before they eat their first meal of blood and most especially before they reproduce and start laying eggs. A flea feeds within minutes after landing on an animal and is capable of laying eggs within one day. Insecticides such as thrinoides, fipronil, or amidacloprid are effective immediately and have satisfactory residual activity. All of these products can be used in formulas that can be applied in just one spot, a method particularly suited to cats. Once a small amount of the product is applied to the skin (typically between the shoulders), it spreads to the rest of the body within one day.

With this type of treatment, a cat is protected for a period of one month. Flea collars currently available on the market only partially control fleas, since they do not prevent infestation in the first place. To eliminate fleas in a cat's environment, it is first necessary to identify all potentially infested areas. Not only should a cat's living area, outside territory and resting areas be considered, but also other animals (other cats, and possibly dogs) with which the cat will come into contact. It is necessary to ensure as much as possible that all animals encountered by the cat are treated on a regular basis. This is, of course, impossible if your cat has the habit of socializing with strays.

Formulations used in living areas typically combine an insecticide with a growth regulator, which interferes with the normal development of immature fleas. Foggers (flea "bombs") treat a large area. Sprays should be used as a supplement to foggers in order to treat hard-

Flea
(Source - Mérial Laboratories)

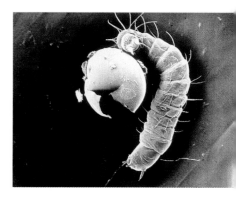

Hatching flea
(Source - Mérial Laboratories)

to-reach areas, such as under furniture. Lufeneron is an insect growth regulator administered orally once a month or injected once every six months. The product enters the bloodstream.

Once an adult flea ingests the chemical, the lufeneron interrupts the development cycle. Eggs do not hatch or larvae die. One of the advantages of this product is that it has a secondary effect of controlling fleas in the environment, though it is only administered to the cat carrying adult fleas.

Ringworm

A common skin disorder in cats is dermatophytosis, or ringworm, caused by the dermatophyte *Microsporum canis*. Hairs infested by this parasite are literally consumed from the inside out. They become very fragile and break off. The typically well-defined bald patches that appear normally start on the head and then spread outward to the rest of the body.

The infection may resolve itself spontaneously within a few weeks, but other bald patches are likely to appear. In longhair breeds, hairloss may be distributed throughout the coat and only a slight thinning in certain areas may be noted. Ringworm is highly contagious. Fragments of infested hairs transmit the parasite to healthy animals.

These infectious agents are present both on animals showing signs of ringworm as well as in the environment. Direct contact is not necessary. A cat can easily contract the parasite in a dirty environment; from a carpet where a contaminated cat lay down several days earlier, a carrier used to transport a contaminated animal, a brush, or a clipper.

The infectious agents are very resistant. It is believed that *Microsporum canis* can survive for several months (perhaps up to a year) in the external environment. Another unique aspect

of this fungus is its lack of specificity. *Microsporum canis* prefers cats as hosts, but it is also responsible for ringworm in rabbits, dogs, rodents, primates (including humans), and even herbivores. Infected cats are treated with an oral or topical antifungal medication. Treatment must be continued for at least six weeks.

There are few methods for preventing ringworm. A vaccine is currently available in the United States, but its effectiveness remains disputed. Unlike flea treatments, there are no long-acting antifungal treatments that can be applied once a month as a preventive measure. Currently, the best way to protect a cat is to keep her away from infected animals. Though this may appear simple, it is, in fact, quite difficult.

Cats can easily come into contact with strays, which benefit from no health care and often carry dermatophytes. Moreover, it is often difficult to identify cats that may be carrying ringworm fungi, and which are therefore contagious, since some exhibit no symptoms.

Cat shows or any other feline gathering should be considered at-risk areas. To reduce the chances of infection, a topical antifungal treatment should be applied to all cats prior to a show. In a cattery, normal sanitation guidelines should be strictly followed when a new cat is introduced. The newcomer should be quarantined until its health status can be determined. Examination under a Wood's light and a fungal culture will determine if the cat presents a danger to the other residents.

Finally, since ringworm can be transmitted in a dirty environment, carpets, rugs, and upholstery should be vacuumed regularly to eliminate the majority of the dermatophytes. Special solutions and fumigants are also available from veterinarians. These can be used to treat contaminated areas.

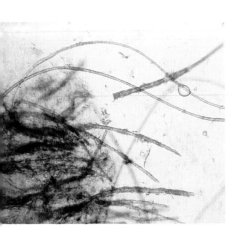

Hairs of a cat infected with ringworm fungi.

Disease	Responsible Agent	Frequency	Transmission	Danger to Humans
Otisis externa	Mites (Otodectes cynotis)	++ (young cats)	Direct (cat to cat)	None
Mange	Mites (Notoedres cati)	Very rare	Direct (cat to cat)	+ (scabies)
Cheyletiellosis	Mites (Cheyletiella blakei)	+	Direct (cat to cat) or from external environment	++ (scabies)
Pulicosis	Fleas (Ctenocephalides felis)	+++	Mostly indirect from a contaminated environment	+ (flea bites)
Pediculosis	Lice (Felicola subrostratus)	+ (young cats)	Direct (cat to cat)	None
Ringworm	Dermatophytes	+++	Direct or indirect from a contaminated environment	++ (ringworm)

Internal Parasites

In addition to external infestations by external parasites such as fleas, lice, and ticks, cats of any age, young and old alike, are susceptible to internal parasitic infestations by worms (helminths) or microbes called protozoa.

It is difficult to determine the frequency of helminths (worms). Studies have produced widely varying results. Cats living in rural areas often have more worms than urban cats. The same is true of indoor/outdoor cats, as compared to indoor cats only. Finally, young cats are more susceptible than adult cats. At-risk cats can be divided into two groups: kittens, from birth to ten months of age; and indoor/outdoor cats living in rural or urban areas (residential areas with yards).

A 1996 study showed that on average one in five cats has worms. This number climbs to one in three in kittens under one year of age.

The primary parasitic worms in cats are ascarids, or roundworms (*Toxocara cati*), anky-lostoma, or hookworms, and some tapeworms, including *Dipylidium*.

Ascarids

Toxocara cati is a roundworm (nematode) 4 to 8 cm in length. It occurs in the small intestine of a cat and forms balls that can cause intestinal irritation or obstruction. Cats can become infected either by ingesting the eggs of the parasites or while nursing in the first ten days following birth.

Infected cats harbor the larvae in their body tissues, including muscle and mammary, their entire lives. For some reason, the larvae become reactivated toward the end of gestation, producing adult intestinal ascarids. Some larvae migrate to the mammary glands where they are carried to the kittens in the milk. Queens also contaminate their environment with the ascarid eggs passed in their feces, another way for the kittens to be infected.

The microscopic eggs, which are passed in large quantities in the cat's feces, are very resis-

Parasite	Epidemiological Information
Ollulanus tricuspis	Strongyloid parasite of the stomach. Rare.
Ackylostoma tubaeformis	Ancylostoma parasite of the duodenum, particularly common in warm climates. Cats become infected by ingesting the larvae or by the larvae penetrating the skin.
Uncimaria stenocephala	Common ancylostoma in dogs. Present in France.
Toxocara cati	Ascarid parasite of the duodenum. Very common in young cats (to the age of one year).
Toxascaris leonina	Ascarid found in adult cats that hunt mice, primarily in rural areas.
Dipylidium caninum	Most frequently observed tenia in cats living in cities or in countryside. Follow the ingestion of fleas.

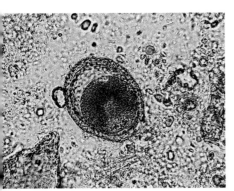

Toxocara cati

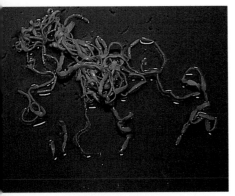

Dipylidium caninum

tant to cold and dry conditions, as well as traditional disinfectants. In fact, they can survive for more than three years on the ground.

After being ingested, the larvae migrate throughout the cat's body, passing through the liver and lungs before returning to the intestine where they develop to adulthood. This cycle lasts approximately six weeks.

Ascarid infections often produce dramatic symptoms. Kittens may have abdominal swelling or experience bouts of diarrhea. Infection may also be associated with poor growth (rickets and dry, dull coat). Adult worms may be found in the vomitus of infected cats. Untreated, it can result in death by peritonitis.

Tapeworms

Dipylidium caninum is a segmented tapeworm (cestode). Fleas carry the larvae of this parasite. Cat's ingest the infected fleas while grooming. Three weeks later, adult worms appear in the intestinal tract. Round or oval shaped segments are expelled with the stool. They can often be seen around the anus or on the cat's fur. These whitish segments are 5 to 6 mm in length and mobile when fresh. After they dry out, they resemble small grains of rice. Owners often think they are seeing pinworms, but this parasite does not exist in cats.

Other worms may also infect cats, appearing after a cat eats prey, particularly mice. These types of worms are most often seen in rural areas.

Worm infestation normally does not cause serious illness in cats, though it can result in malformations or a dull coat, as well as anal pruritis (itching) after segments are expelled.

Preventing Worm Infestation

It is important to limit the risk of infection from the time a kitten is born.

- Queens should be treated with a dewormer fifteen days prior to and one month following delivery.

- Kittens should be treated at the ages of one, three, and six months.

- Cats should then be treated with a dewormer twice per year.

- If toxocarosis is diagnosed within the cattery, kittens should be treated once per month until the age of six months.

Many dewormer treatments are currently on the market. They are available in paste or pill form. The choice is determined by the type of parasite to be eliminated and ease of administration.

In addition to medications, the cat's environment should be thoroughly cleaned to remove eggs. All cats should be monitored and the queens treated with a dewormer.

The risk of Dipylidium infection can be reduced by ridding living areas of fleas. Deworming should only be done if the cat is passing worm segments, is a regular hunter, or is infested with fleas.

Keep in mind that Toxocara cati, like ascarids in dogs (Toxocara canis), can be transmitted to humans and cause serious illness (zoonoses). This may occur if the owner or breeder ingests the larval eggs present in the environment.

Common Protozoa

Even very young cats can be infected with digestive parasites other than worms. Two categories of protozoa are observed in cats: Giardia and coccidia. These protozoa occur as frequently as worms and infect 30 to 60% of all kittens in catteries, compared to 5 to 20% of kittens in private homes.

When the Giardia protozoa multiply, they irritate the intestinal lining (enteritis) and inhibit digestion and absorption, resulting in weight loss and chronic diarrhea. Young and old cats alike are vulnerable to Giardia. Cysts are expelled with fecal matter, the source of contamination of other individuals.

After a confirmed diagnosis, Giardiasis may be treated with drugs such as metronidazole or fenbendazole.

There are many coccidian protozoa found in cats. The most common are Isospora, which cause acute enteritis in young cats between the ages of one and six months. Cat are infected when they ingest the oocysts present on the ground. Another method of infection, though less common, is ingestion of rodents (particularly mice).

Other coccidian protozoa are ingested when cats eat their prey. These include Besnoitia, hammondia, and Toxoplasma gondii. Toxoplasma gondii, the protozoa responsible

DEWORMER TREATMENTS

Active Ingredient	Product Name	Form	Worms Treated
Piperazine	Ascaperazine®	Syrup	Ascarids
Pyrantel	Strongid®	Oral compound	Ascarids, ancylostoma
Oxibendazole + Niclosamide	Vitaminthe®	Oral compound	Ascarids, ancylostoma, *Taeina* and *Dipylidium* (minimal dose required for satisfactory effectiveness on *Dipylidium*)
Flubendazole	Flubenol®	Oral compound	Ascarids, ancylostoma, *Taenia*
Praziquantel	Droncit® Droncit®Pill Plativers®	Tablet (microtablet for Droncit®Pill), or sub-cutaneous injection	Cestodes (including *Dilpilydium*, Mesocestodes, *Taenia*, and *Echinococcus*)
Pyrantel + Praziquantel	Drontal®Chat	Tablet	Ascarids, ancylostoma and cestodes (*Taenia* and *Dipylidium*)

for toxoplasmosis, can infect all mammals, including humans. The cat is the only host that harbors intestinal forms and expels the cysts. Other mammals, including humans, are infected by ingesting cysts eliminated by cats, or, as is more often the case, by consuming other infected animals (mutton, pork, and occasionally beef). Approximately 90% of all adult cats have been infected with Toxoplasma.

Most coccidian protozoa have little effect on cats and infections are typically asymptomatic. Only Isospora are likely to cause serious diarrhea in young kittens.
Coccidian protozoa are treated with trimethoprime-enhanced sulfonamides (sulfa drugs).

The best way to prevent protozoan infection is through good sanitation. The floors of the cattery should be cleaned regularly to reduce the number of cysts in the environment. Testing and treating adult carriers (often queens) is also an important part of an overall prevention plan.

Digestive parasites are common in cats. Fortunately, the frequency and seriousness of infections can be reduced by implementing appropriate treatment, both in catteries and in private homes. Worms are prevented through regular deworming (twice-yearly treatment is recommended). If in doubt, consult your veterinarian, who can test your cat and confirm or rule out parasitic infection.

Vaccinations

Owners who are concerned about the health of their cats must have their pets vaccinated to protect them from serious illness.

The prevalence of several serious cat diseases has declined in recent years, due in large part to the availability of a wide range of effective vaccines. Though the number of cats vaccinated each year is on the rise, in France cats receive less medical attention than dogs and therefore are not as well protected by preventive vaccines.

Certain common cat diseases almost always result in death. Others only rarely threaten the life of the animal, but it is always preferable to avoid potential disease by vaccinating the cat.

Of all vaccines available, some vaccines are essential, others are strongly recommended, and others are recommended in certain situations. Unfortunately, there is not an effective vaccine for every disease that has been identified to date.

Zoonoses (anthropozoonoses) are diseases shared by humans and animals. The primary diseases that can be transmitted from cats to humans or vice versa are: Rabies, toxoplasmosis, tuberculosis, and cat-scratch disease. None currently present a serious threat. Rabies is effectively controlled as the result of mandatory vaccination in certain circumstances (see below).

About Vaccines

A brief review of immunology

The organism's reaction to a foreign substance is to develop a response to counter the invader. This response is referred to as an immunological or immune response. The body mounts its defense with white blood cells called lymphocytes, which create a response specific to each antigen.

Lymphocytes have specialized roles. Some, such as B-cells, produce antibodies to neutralize infectious agents. Others, such as T-cells, directly attach infected cells in an effort to destroy them. In both cases, the lymphocytes "remember" this initial contact with the foreign body, and if they come into contact with this same foreign body again, they can respond immediately and destroy it even before it has a chance to multiply and produce illness (if it is a pathogenic agent).

Therefore, if an animal has had contact with the foreign body, whether through natural contact or vaccination, the animal is generally protected. The level of protection is determined by several factors, the antibodies being the most important mode of defense.

Age and Vaccinations

Kittens

A kitten's immunocompetence, that is, its ability to develop a good immune response, is complete by the second or third week of life. In theory, kitten may be vaccinated after the age of 15 days, though in reality, in most cases, vaccinations given to kittens are cancelled out by interference from immunity passed on from the mother.

Geriatric Cats

Over time, the number of antibodies produced by a cat's immune system decreases and its immune system weakens. Therefore, it is important to administer booster vaccinations to geriatric cats.

Vaccinations for Cats

Nature of vaccines

Indications and contraindications.

In general, it is contraindicated to vaccinate cats that are ill, infected with parasites, or undergoing treatment with an immunodepressant. Kittens as a rule should be treated with a dewormer before any vaccinations are administered. Moreover, modified (attenuated) vaccines are contraindicated for gestating females, since, until evidence to the contrary, it is believed that they may cause abnormalities in the fetus.

Cats that go outdoors are at higher risk of contracting disease through contact with other cats or other contaminated areas. Therefore, vaccination is all the more important. However, it should not be assumed that a sedentary indoor cat is not at risk and therefore does not require vaccination. Even indoor cats that will never have direct contact with other animals can be exposed. Contaminants from other infected animals can be brought in on the sole of a shoe, for example. It is also important to keep in mind that even a cat that "never goes out" will on occasion leave the house, whether for a trip to the veterinarian, to a kennel, or for travel, when the owners move, for example. If a cat has not been vaccinated and is exposed to contaminated areas, such as waiting rooms, kennels, or the interior of a car, he is at high risk.

One of the difficulties of defining vaccination requirements is that some infections have an asymptomatic stage during which a cat shows no clinical signs of infection, even when examined by a veterinarian, but is still able to contaminate other cats with which he comes into contact. Animals with infections such as rhinitis and chlamydiosis may appear cured, but may in fact be carriers and potentially excrete the pathogenic agent responsible for the disease.

Other infections develop slowly. The infected cat appears to be in good health, but is actually simply in the asymptomatic stage of the disease. Without administering a specialized test to identify the specific disease, the cat cannot be diagnosed and will pose a risk to other cats. All of these possible opportunities for infection demonstrate the interest of ensuring that a cat is vaccinated.

When a cat is vaccinated, the veterinarian will record the type, method, date, and lot number of the vaccination in the cat's vaccination record. Only a veterinarian is authorized to enter this information.

The Age Factor: Kittens

In carnivores, 90 to 95% of the mother's antigens are passed on to her offspring through her first milk, or colostrum. When kittens first nurse, they receive almost all the mother's antibodies, built up throughout her life through contact with infectious agents and vaccinations. Her complete immunologic heritage is passed on to her offspring. The immunity resulting from this process is called passive immunity. During this phase, the kitten is not yet producing his own antibodies.
The intestinal barrier is highly permeable, allowing the antibodies of the colostrum to enter the kitten's circulatory system in the first two days of life.

The concentration of antibodies in the kitten's blood decreases gradually and is undetectable by the age of two and a-half months on average. This period varies from kitten to kitten and is influenced by several factors, the most important being the concentration of antibodies in the mother's milk and the size of the litter.

The positive aspect of this transmission process is that the mother's antigens will protect the kittens during the first weeks of life. However, unfortunately, these same antibodies can interfere with early vaccinations. By combining with the vaccine's antigens, these antibodies cancel out the immunization that would normally result following vaccination.

The critical period is the time between which the kitten becomes vulnerable to natural infection and the moment that he can be effectively vaccinated. This is a dangerous time for kittens, who are surrounded by a multitude of potentially infectious agents. The viruses in their physical surroundings are highly resistant, especially the feline panleukopenia. The solution is to begin vaccinations at the age of six weeks and repeat them every two weeks until the age of twelve to fourteen weeks. This "heavy-handed" approach is particularly suitable for kittens in catteries where disease has been identified. Kittens in private homes are at lesser risk, particularly since they have typically received their first round of shots prior to being sold.

Types of Vaccines

Some vaccines have been around for a long time and are commonly used. Others have been developed only recently, using advanced technologies. These are the wave of the future.

Traditional vaccines include inactivated (dead) and attenuated (modified, live) vaccines.

Inactivated vaccines are prepared using bacterial or viral agents treated by heat or chemicals. When developing a new vaccine, it is necessary to first create an inactive vaccine since the casual agent has not yet been stabilized in a non-virulent form, as is the case with the rabies vaccine, for example.

In live vaccines, the agent is modified so that it no longer produces clinical disease. However, it is still able to multiply. As a result, the vaccinated animal produces a strong immune response. These are considered highly immunogenic (producing immunity) vaccines.

Vaccines prepared using today's **advanced technologies** promise a bright future for vaccinations. In fact, a vaccine of this type for feline leukemia is already available on the market.

Vaccination Calendar

A veterinarian can set up a vaccination calendar that takes into account the various needs of each individual cat, considering lifestyle, age, and environment. However, some general principles apply.

The biggest challenge is vaccinating kittens as soon as possible after passive immunity has waned. In order to do this, two series of injections are required. The first is administered between six and ten weeks of age (typically at eight weeks of age), followed by a second round three to four weeks later, between the ages of twelve and fourteen weeks. Current legislation on rabies vaccination stipulates that kittens are not to be vaccinated until three months of age.

Vaccinated cats require booster shots from time to time in order to maintain effective immunity.

Disease Prevention

Mandatory Vaccination

All cats must be vaccinated against rabies.

Rabies is a form of viral encephalomyelitis common to all warm-blooded animals (including humans). It is one of the most feared zoonoses, because it is always fatal. The illness begins with an incubation period lasting thirty days on average, after which symptoms of nervous disorder appear. Death occurs within three to six days. Rabies is classified as an infectious disease and vaccination is regulated. Outdoor cats are most at risk. However, the prevalence of rabies has decreased dramatically in recent years in France, markedly decreasing risk of infection. All cats entering France from a foreign country must be vaccinated, as must cats travelling from infected departments within France. In addition, rabies vaccination is required if owners wish to bring their cats into a campground or enter their cat in a cat show.

French law stipulates that kittens must not be vaccinated until the age of three months. Since complete protection is not assured until one month following vaccination, requests for access to areas where vaccination is required (campgrounds, cat shows, border crossings) cannot be approved until the cat reaches four months of age.

Recommended Vaccinations

Currently, most cats are vaccinated against rabies, panleukopenia, viral rhinotracheitis, and leukemia (see table on page 421).

In the past, **feline panleukopenia** took the life of many cats. However, the disease is now rare in urban areas, thanks to a widespread vaccination program. Most panleukopenia vaccines available on the French market are modified vaccines. Vaccination of queens during the third trimester and kittens under the age of four weeks is contraindicated.

Feline viral rhinotracheitis (FVR) is an acute infectious disease caused primarily by two different viruses acting alone or in concert. Symptoms cannot be linked to the specific responsible agent. Therefore, all symptoms are grouped under the heading rhinotracheitis. As noted in the introduction to this section, cats are at risk of exposure, and therefore disease, from asymptomatic carriers. One purified subunit vaccine and several modified vaccines are available in France.

Feline leukemia is caused by the FeLV virus, one of two viruses causing immunodeficiency in cats, the other being Feline Immunodeficiency Virus, or FIV. Symptoms of feline leukemia typically appear two years following infection. FIV leads to acquired immunodeficiency syndrome **(Feline AIDS)** eight to ten years following infection.

Both diseases present with generalized symptoms, including weight loss, fever, general decline, and appetite loss, accompanied by a wide array of localized infections.

A vaccine is available only for feline leukemia, not FIV. Cats at risk of exposure to FelV can be protected against this deadly disease by being vaccinated. However, the vaccine is only effective in FeLV-negative cats, though it will not harm cats already infected with the virus. Vaccination does not interfere with blood test results and diagnosis. Diagnosis is based on the presence of viral antigens, not antibodies fighting the virus.

Chlamydiosis is a bacterial disease producing conjunctivitis and sometimes accompanied by runny nose and cough. The bacteria may act alone or in conjunction with the rhinotracheitis virus, aggravating FVR symptoms. Cats that have contracted this disease and appear to be cured carry the virus for an extended period of time and may excrete the virus, with or without symptoms, posing a threat of infection to other cats.

Vaccines are not available for the following diseases in France

Feline Infectious Peritonitis (FIP) is a serious viral infection. In the most common form,

effusive FIP, fluid accumulates in the abdomen, enlarging the abdomen. In France, individuals purchasing kittens are protected by law and are entitled a refund if they purchase a kitten that is later diagnosed with FIP. There is no authorized vaccine available in France for this disease. Until recently, all FIP vaccination trials were unsuccessful. However, an attenuated FIP virus strain was recently isolated. When administered by the intranasal route, its effectiveness seems to be promising. This product has already been approved in the United States and some European countries. In France, additional studies are required before approval can be granted.

There is currently no vaccine available to protect the cat against FIV, which leads to feline AIDS, though much research is currently under way. This feline disease is very similar to AIDS in humans, and as a result, the advantages of such research are two-fold, benefiting the fields of both veterinary and comparative medicine. If an effective vaccine were devel-

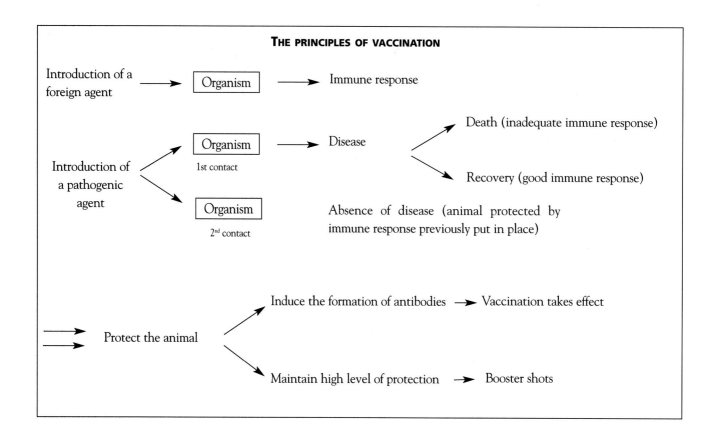

THE PRINCIPLES OF VACCINATION

Introduction of a foreign agent → Organism → Immune response

Introduction of a pathogenic agent → Organism 1st contact → Disease → Death (inadequate immune response) / Recovery (good immune response)

Organism 2nd contact → Absence of disease (animal protected by immune response previously put in place)

Protect the animal → Induce the formation of antibodies → Vaccination takes effect / Maintain high level of protection → Booster shots

oped for FIV, this accomplishment would be of great interest to researchers working on a vaccine for humans.

Vaccination is a simple, generally harmless method for protecting cats from serious infectious diseases. In order to protect the health of their beloved companions, all owners must ensure that their cats are vaccinated in accordance with their veterinarian's recommendations.

FELINE VACCINES AVAILABLE IN FRANCE

		Viral Diseases	Bacterial Diseases
Inactivated vaccines	Traditional	Rhinotracheitis (two valences) Leukemia Rabies	Chlamydiosis
Live vaccines	Traditional Nasal route	Panleukopenia Rhinotracheitis (two valences) Infectious Peritonitis*	Chlamydiosis
By intranasal route Subunit vaccines	Portion of the infectious agent obtained through genetic engineering	Herpesvirus valence of rhinotracheitis Leukemia	
*Not yet approved in France at the time of this writing.			

Common Diseases

Owners love their cats and want to keep them healthy and happy. It is important that owners be familiar with the following diseases and the symptoms that should prompt a visit to the veterinarian.

A healthy kitten looks alert and has a full, clean, soft coat. His gait is relaxed. The ears contain only a small quantity of light brown ear wax. The eyes are well open and do not tear. Breathing is not labored, and the mouth and tongue look healthy and smell sweet. The area around the anus is clean. In male cats that have not been neutered, the two testicles have descended normally into the scrotum. Cats exude a distinctive feline odor, but the odor is not disagreeable.

Sick cat

Even the most careful exam will not reveal diseases invisible to the naked eye, so a visit to the veterinarian for a thorough exam and any necessary tests is advisable.

The food a kitten eats has an impact on his health. Commercial foods provide a healthy, balanced diet for cats at all stages of life, and as a result, bone disorders in growing kittens are now rare. However, feeding an all-protein diet or administering vitamins incorrectly (overdose of Vitamin E, for example) can cause osteofibrosis, in which the fragile bones are prone to greenstick or other serious fractures.

At the age of three months, the fully weaned kitten is capable of feeding himself and is well adapted to his environment. It is the owner's responsibility to provide the nourishment and care required for healthy growth.

Viral and Bacterial Infections

Once a kitten is no longer protected by the antibodies provided by his mother during gestation and nursing, he is vulnerable to viral and bacterial infections.

Leukemia and Feline Immunodeficiency

Cats are vulnerable to several infectious agents responsible for frequently fatal diseases. The most serious are three viruses: Feline Leukemia Virus (FeLV), Feline Immunodeficiency Virus (FIV), and Feline Infectious Peritonitis (FIP).

The first two, FeLV and FIV, are caused by a retrovirus.

Since the mode of transmission and susceptibility differs with each disease and each cat, it is impossible to say that only specific populations are at risk.

FeLV is transmitted through contact, licking, and use of a common litter box. The animals most at risk are kittens or young adults, indoor/outdoor cats, and/or those living in multiple-cat households.

FIV is transmitted primarily through bites. FIV infection is rare in catteries. It is much more common in free-roaming cats. Older, intact, indoor/outdoor males are the most at risk.

If a susceptible cat comes into contact with FeLV, the virus may be immediately eradicated by the body and not result in symptoms. However, if the virus escapes the body's initial immune defenses, it will enter the bloodstream. The presence of the virus in the bloodstream is called viremia.

If the body's immune response is sufficient, the spread of the virus is halted, but the virus may remain in bone marrow cells. If the virus overwhelms the body's immune defenses, it spreads throughout the organism, and the disease develops.

Symptoms vary considerably and follow an asymptomatic phase during which the cat is contagious. Anemia sets in, mucous membranes turn pale, the cat tires easily and is winded quickly. Since the body's immune defenses are weakened, the cat is at risk for a variety of complications, including respiratory viral infections, abscesses, chronic diarrhea, or skin disorders. Any cat with recurring illness or an illness not responding to treatment should be tested for retroviruses. Reproductive disorders are a classic symptom, as are tumors (especially lymphomas).

The clinical progression of FIV infection corresponds to a progressive weakening of the immune system, which can be divided into five stages, as follows:

- primo-infection - low-grade fever and swollen glands
- asymptomatic carrier (seropositive)

- early clinical stage - onset of symptoms, including hairloss and fever (this phase lasts several months)
- consolidation - appearance of major, recurring infections that respond poorly or not at all to treatment (this phase lasts several months)
- terminal - the cat is vulnerable to all germs, even those that are not highly infectious; onset of a wide variety of infections, resulting in death within one to six months

It is not uncommon for a cat infected with FeLV to be infected with FIV as well. These cats typically suffer from extremely serious diseases and die shortly after symptoms first appear.

There is no effective treatment for retroviruses, though several treatments are available that may prolong an infected cat's life, including corticosteroids and antimitotic drugs. Treatment of secondary infections with antibiotics simply postpones death.

Feline Infectious Peritonitis

Feline Infectious Peritonitis, FIP for short, takes two forms - effusive (wet) and noneffusive (dry). The causal agent is a virus belonging to the family Coronaviridae.

While the incidence of FIP is higher among purebred cats, this seems to be caused by environment (confinement) rather than a genetic predisposition. Nevertheless, some lines seem to be more susceptible than others.

FIP is a serious, deadly concern for breeders, animal shelters, and areas where many cats live together, particularly if kittens are present. Cats of all ages contract FIP, though it is more common in kittens and young cats up to one and a half year of age. The primary route of transmission is oral-fecal. A susceptible cat is infected through licking or through contact with the excreta of an infected cat. It is thought that airborne transmission of the virus is possible, though researchers have not determined whether fleas and other insect bites can spread the disease.

It is likely that some cats that have come into contact with the virus are healthy carriers who excrete the virus on occasion, in times of stress, illness, or during reproduction. The FIP virus is highly resistant and can survive outside the body for several weeks.

There are different strains of feline coronaviruses (FcoV), from very mild (unnoticed infection), to moderately severe (causing enteritis), and the highly virulent strains responsible for clinical FIP. Depending on the strain contracted, the mortality rate ranges from 0% to 100%. Most strains are only moderately virulent. The viruses responsible for clinical FIP are probably mutations of FcoV.

Following infection by a feline coronavirus, the following symptoms may appear:

• An asymptomatic infection or moderate intestinal infection; the cat tests positive and is often a healthy carrier

• An isolated abdominal or ocular inflammation

• Full-fledged peritonitis; only 1% to 10% of all cats infected with a feline coronavirus develop FIP symptoms, the most serious form of the disease. FIP is almost always fatal.

Incubation ranges from one to two days up to several years. Two major forms of FIP exist: Effusive, in which fluid builds up in body cavities, and noneffusive. The clinical signs of the noneffusive form vary depending on the organ(s) affected (encephalitis, for example). Symptoms are treated to slow the progression of the disease, but no cure currently exists.

Feline Panleukopenia Virus

This disease, commonly referred to as distemper, is caused by a highly resistant parvovirus capable of surviving outside the body for more than one year. Cats are infected when they come into contact with an infected animal or an area where the virus is present.

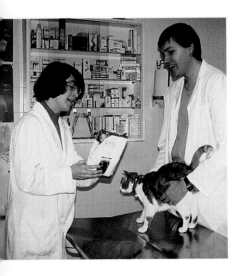

TESTING FOR FeLV AND FIV

How are the FeLV and FIV retroviruses detected?

Testing confirms or rules out the presence of a retrovirus. Testing can also identify healthy carriers so that contagious cats are not introduced to healthy environments. FeLV tests analyze a cat's blood to detect presence of the virus. A test can be false-positive in the first few weeks following exposure. The reverse is also true—a cat testing positive can test negative at a later date. Therefore, the test should be administered twice at a three month interval.

The test for FIV looks for the presence of FIV antibodies in the blood. One hundred percent of all cats showing antibodies in the blood are infected with FIV. Therefore, there is no need to repeat this test.

How is FIP diagnosed?

The tests currently available in France detect the antibodies produced by the cat's body in reaction to contact with a feline coronavirus. These tests are effective for diagnosing FIP (in conjunction with other clinical elements). They can also be used to protect a healthy cat population, ensuring that only seronegative cats are introduced to the group.

These tests do have their limitations. False positives can result from vaccinations, maternal antibodies, or other coronaviruses. False negatives are possible in the case of in utero infection, slow spread of the virus, or a temporarily seronegative healthy carrier. In addition, several techniques may be used, and therefore results may differ from one laboratory to the next.

Symptoms vary, depending primarily on the age of the animal. Young cats are typically the most seriously affected.

In the most severe cases, an infected cat may die suddenly, within less than twelve hours following infection.

The acute form of FPV is characterized by a high fever and severe depression. The animal refuses to eat and vomiting and diarrhea occur, resulting in dehydration. Blood tests show a dramatic drop in the white blood count.

The mortality rate varies from 50% to 60%. Animals that recover from FPV sometimes suffer from recurring bouts of diarrhea.

If a gestating queen is infected with a wild virus or vaccinated with a live attenuated virus, the virus is capable of infecting the fetus. If infection occurs in the early stages of gestation, the fetuses will be aborted. During the second trimester, the infection will cause hypoplasia—underdevelopment of the cerebellum. Clinic signs appear when the kittens reach approximately four weeks of age. They begin trembling, lack coordination, and are unable to move about.

There is no treatment for the form of FPV affecting kittens. For older cats, a veterinarian will rehydrate the sick animal using an IV, treat the symptoms, and administer antibiotics to limit complications from secondary infections. Prognosis is guarded and mortality is high.

Rabies

The occurrence of this disease, which reared its ugly head again in France in 1968, is dropping as a result of effective health measures including vaccination of domestic animals and fox, and monitoring of biting animals.

Rabies is a form of encephalitis (inflammation of the brain) caused by a rhabdovirus.

The primary means of rabies virus transmission is the bite of an infected animal. The virus enters through the break in the skin caused by the bite. The length of incubation varies from several weeks to several months. Rabies is always fatal once clinical signs appear. If bitten by an animal showing clinical signs of rabies or suspected of being infected with the rabies virus, treatment with a rabies virus antiserum must begin immediately during the incubation period.

Rabies in cats produces dramatic clinical symptoms, including paralysis and complete prostration. Most often, rabid cats go through a furious stage during which they are wild and aggressive.

Strict laws have been imposed in the attempt to prevent the spread of rabies in humans and animals. Any animal that has bitten or scratched a human must be quarantined and observed by a veterinarian for a period of fifteen days.

Eye and Upper Respiratory Disorders

The most serious of these are caused by three viruses and a chlamydia bacterial agent. All survive no more than 48 hours outside the body, except caliciviruses, which are capable of living up to ten days. As a result, these illnesses are typically not transmitted by simple contact with the virus in the environment, but instead, are passed directly from cat to cat.

Clinical signs are similar to those of a cold in humans. Common symptoms include fever, followed rapidly by conjunctivitis and tearing, sneezing, and sometimes a runny nose and a cough. Some symptoms point to specific agents, but it is not uncommon for multiple infections to occur in the same cat.

Feline viral rhinotracheitis is caused by feline herpesvirus type 1. Symptoms include paroxysmal sneezing, nasal discharge, tearing with corneal ulcers, and lesions on the tongue. Infected pregnant cats frequently abort. Mortality is high among kittens and adults in a weakened condition.

Eighty percent of all cats that recover are carriers. They harbor the dormant virus in their bodies, but show no clinical signs. During times of stress, these cats may excrete the virus.

The symptoms of feline calicivirus vary depending on the particular strain of calicivirus responsible for the illness as well as the health of the infected cat's immune system.
In the mildest cases, symptoms are limited to ulcers on the tongue, palate, lips, and nasal septum. Due to the pain caused by the ulcers, the cat refuses to eat. Tearing and runny nose are also common. In more severe cases, onset of pneumonia may lead to death (the mortality rate in kittens is 100%). Less commonly, symptoms include contracture of the toes and stiff gait caused by joint and muscle pain.
Once cured, some cats completely eliminate the virus from their body, while others remain carriers.

Reovirus infection is caused by a reovirus. Conjunctivitis is typically the only symptom and complications are rare. No vaccine exists.

Chlamydia psittaci is the causal agent for feline **chlamydiosis**. The first signs of infection are conjunctivitis and chemosis (edema of the ocular conjunctiva) affecting only one eye, then spreading to the other. These symptoms sometimes disappear without treatment. In the most severe cases, these symptoms worsen after ten to twelve days and the cat begins coughing and sneezing. Pregnant queens sometimes abort. Complete recovery takes two to six weeks.

Cats that have recovered from the illness are sometimes asymptomatic carriers that excrete the chlamydial bacteria in times of stress.

A veterinarian will prescribe antibiotics and treat the symptoms. Attentive care is required. Since the cat's air passages are blocked, he will not eat voluntarily nor clean himself. It is imperative that he be made to eat (force fed if necessary). Wet foods and soups or liquid specialty nutritional formulas are appropriate, as prescribed by a veterinarian. Feeding, cleaning, clearing nasal passages, and administering inhalations will speed recovery. Aerosol inhalations can be administered at home or in a veterinarian's office.

Digestive System Disorders

The health of the **digestive tract** depends first and foremost on the health of the teeth. Over the years, tartar builds up on teeth. The mineral salts contained in saliva are deposited on dental plaque present on teeth forming a hard stonelike concretion sealed by bacteria present in the mouth. Tartar buildup pushes on the gingiva (gums) causing inflammation, infection, and eventually resulting in periodontitis. Tartar must be removed. In severe cases, it may be necessary to remove some teeth, which can lead to problems in the future.
Many adult and geriatric cats suffer from osteoclastic or tooth resorption. Initially, areas of depression appear at the neck of the tooth. As resorption progresses, the teeth become fragile and then break. The roots may also be eliminated, but sometimes remain in the gingiva, resulting in the potential for chronic gingivitis. Cats with advanced cases drool continuously and refuse to eat. When food is put down, the cat rushes to the bowl, but refuses to take even one bite or takes a bite, but paws at his mouth as if to remove a foreign body. Early lesions can be treated, but once the dental pulp is involved, extraction of the tooth is normally the only option.

The **esophagus** propels food to the stomach through the cardia, the opening into the stomach. If the cardia does not function properly, food piles up in the lower end of the esophagus and is eventually regurgitated. This can also occur if a tumor in the chest or a vascular arch present at birth compresses the esophagus. Over time, this buildup of food stretches the esophagus, a condition called megaesophagus. Typically, kittens swallow maternal milk easily. The problem appears when they begin eating solid food. Mild cases can be treated with changes to the diet, but generally, the prognosis is grim.

The cat's **stomach** may be the seat of acute and chronic disorders, gastritis, but is also involved in other pathological disorders.
Acute gastritis may follow ingestion of unhealthful, medicated, toxic, or nonfood substances. It may also be a clinical sign of other disorders, including allergies, liver, kidney, or heart disorders, or infectious or parasitic illnesses.

The most benign cases result in a twenty-four hour fast (no more), after which the cat slowly begins eating again. More serious cases require the care of a veterinarian in order to control vomiting and administer treatment appropriate to the causal agent.

Chronic gastritis accompanied by occasional vomiting, weight loss, and food intolerance can also appear alone or in conjunction with other symptoms.

Long-term treatment involves more than the administration of medications. Changes must be made to the diet, such as feeding several small meals per day of concentrated, hypoallergenic food. Additional tests, such as x-rays, barium transit, or exploratory fibroscopy or exploratory laparotomy, are required for accurate diagnosis. Gastric ulcers are uncommon and difficult to identify.

Stomach torsion, a very serious condition in dogs, is extremely rare in cats.

Problems in the **small intestine** can result in diarrhea.

Acute diarrhea can be caused by diet. If a cat's food is suddenly changed, the microbial balance in the digestive tract is upset. Certain bacteria develop at the expense of others, producing toxic waste that irritates the intestinal mucosa.

Several viruses cause acute diarrhea, including FIP, feline panleukopenia virus and coronavirus. Young kittens often suffer severe complications after the onset of acute diarrhea: Intussusception (the prolapse, or telescoping, of one part of the intestine into an immediately adjoining part) may occur, requiring emergency surgery to correct the problem. Equally serious are intestinal occlusion or obstruction, rarely caused by a foreign body, because cats taste their food and almost never swallow small objects. The more common cause is a tumor in or near the digestive tract (lymphosarcomas, for example).

The intestine is a favored site for many parasites, the most common being worms such as *ascaris* or *dipylidium*. These bothersome parasites cause diarrhea, digestive disorders, and weight loss. In cases of severe infestation, they may even completely block the intestinal lumen, resulting in intestinal occlusion.

Chronic enteritis may follow an acute illness or appear spontaneously. A sick animal typically has difficulty absorbing the nutrients in the intestine. Enteritis is also one of the clinical signs of other diseases, including diabetes and chronic kidney failure.

Depending on their cause, some cases of chronic enteritis can be treated or alleviated with medication. An appropriate diet is vital in all cases. Such a diet contains easily-digestible, high-quality proteins, and very limited amounts of saturated fat and lactose. Specially formulated commercial foods are almost always prescribed.

Identifying the cause of chronic enteritis is difficult. Invasive tests, such as a biopsy of the intestinal mucosa, are almost always required. Tumors affecting the small intestine cause chronic diarrhea before other signs appear, such as weight loss, abnormal palpation, or compression of neighboring organs.

Exocrine pancreatic insufficiency is rare in cats. In this disease, insufficient excretion of pancreatic juices impairs digestion of fats, carbohydrates, and, to a lesser extent, proteins. The cat loses weight, though constantly hungry, and passes soft, pale, voluminous stools. Supplementing each meal with digestive enzymes and feeding a special diet typically allows a cat to lead a normal life.

Colitis is the inflammation of the large intestine (colon). In acute or chronic colitis, the cat passes soft, voluminous, slimy stools, sometimes flecked with blood. Many things can cause colitis, including infection, parasites, and stress. Sometimes the cause cannot be determined. Hairballs are sometimes at fault. Treatment varies depending on the origin of the problem

Finally, the **rectum** and the **anus**, the end of the digestive tract, are involved in some diseases. Some kittens are born with an anus with no opening to the outside of the body, a serious condition since the kitten is unable to defecate.
Geriatric, obese, and sedentary cats often suffer from constipation. If left untreated and no adjustment is made to the cat's diet, constipation can lead to a condition called coprostasis (accumulation of fecal matter in the rectum) and intestinal occlusion. Medical treatment including laxatives and enemas generally resolve the problem, but serious cases may require surgical intervention.

Causes of Acute Diarrhea in Cats (Cotard)

• Food: Changes in diet, food allergies, food intolerance, overeating.
• Toxins: Particularly acetaminophen (the ingredient in aspirin).

• Viruses: Panleukopenia , FIP, enteritic coronavirus, FeLV, FIV, rotavirus, astrovirus.

• Bacteria: Salmonella, *Campylobacter, Yersinia*, E-coli, *Mycobacterium tuberculosis*.

• Parasites: *Ascaris*, hookworm, whipworm, coccidia, yeast.

• Other: Partial blockage, foreign bodies, such as string, wire, needles.

Causes of Chronic Diarrhea in Cats (Paragon)

• Excess water in the intestines: Overload of the intestines, inadequate digestion, inadequate absorption; pancreatic or biliary insufficiency; lactase deficiency; tumor or inflammation of the intestinal epithelium or intestinal wall.

• Excess secretions from the glands of the intestines: Bacterial toxins, viruses, bacteria, parasites, or toxins (as in acute diarrhea).

• Intestinal motricity (movement): Peristaltic seizing, insufficient fiber, partial obstruction.

Primary Causes of Constipation in Cats (Fayolle)

• Thickened consistency of stools: Ingestion of hair or litter, dehydration.

• Blockage: Obstacle outside the intestine (pelvic fracture, tumor, dry fecal matter around the anus).

• Neuromuscular disorders: Malfunction of the central nervous system or the nerves in the colon (resulting in a condition called megacolon); idiopathic (unknown origin), feline autonomic dysfunction.

• Refusal to defecate: Dirty litter, change in environment, hospitalization, pain when squatting; anal/rectal lesions (anal glands, foreign body, tumor, abscess).

• Some medications

Respiratory System

The respiratory system is the target of specific infectious agents. Rhinitis, tracheitis, bronchitis, and pneumonia are often caused by viral infections.

In serious cases, cats may have difficulty breathing (dyspnea). Certain diseases such as leukemia, in which a lymphoma in the chest may inhibit free movement of the lungs, and FIP, resulting in pleurisy, may also cause breathing difficulty.

If a cat coughs, she may be suffering from one of these infections or feline asthma. A cough is the symptom of a disorder in the airways—larynx, trachea, and bronchi. A cough is typically observed when other organs in the chest are diseased, such as congestive heart failure with pulmonary edema.

An acute cough is caused by irritation in the upper respiratory system (tonsillitis, laryngitis, tracheitis, normally caused by infection, or swallowing difficulties), or, less commonly, by lower respiratory disorders, including infections, acute pulmonary edema, inhalation of irritants, or asthma.

A cough is not always caused by a problem in the respiratory system. An acute cough may also result from cardiovascular disorders.

Chronic upper respiratory disorders are normally caused by acute disorders, as described above, which take hold and become chronic. They may also be caused by problems at the level of the trachea: For example, a foreign object in the trachea, collapse of the trachea, compression of the trachea from an outside source, such as a tumor between the lungs.

The condition of the cardiovascular system should also be considered. Congestive heart failure causes pulmonary edema, which, in combination with the resulting enlargement of the heart, compresses neighboring organs. This compression may lead to a chronic cough.

Asthma in Cats

The term cat asthma refers to recurring episodes of paroxysmal coughing, wheezing, and shortness of breath. This syndrome resembles human asthma in many respects. Feline asthma probably stems from an allergic reaction to allergens inhaled into the lungs, resulting in inflammation of the airways and contraction of the smooth muscles of the airways. Sometimes the coughing fit is so violent that the cat vomits or coughs up digestive juices. Some particularly serious episodes require emergency medical care. A cat suffering from a severe asthma attack lies flat on the ground with elbows held apart and neck extended. The mouth is open with the tongue sticking out. Sometimes, the tongue takes on a blue hue from oxygen deprivation.

The problem is caused by hyper-reactive airways, which contract (bronchospasms) and become inflamed when they come into contact with airborne allergens. Antibiotics have little affect on this type of respiratory disorder, since infectious agents are not the causative factor, though in the case of secondary infections, antibiotics may be appropriate. Anti-inflammatory steroids generally control the attacks and improve the overall health of the cat suffering from asthma.

Cardiovascular Diseases

Cardiovascular disease can afflict cats of all ages, young and old alike. Young cats may be born with deformed hearts, whereas adult and geriatric cats are prone to certain diseases specific to cats. Cats are not likely to experience myocardial infarction due to the positioning of their coronary arteries

Congenital heart defects are not common in felines, though when they do appear, they are often very serious, retarding growth, limiting activity, and causing cyanosis (bluish discoloration of the skin and mucous membranes) with even minimal exertion. Cats suffering from a heart defect often die at a young age. The most common deformities include ventricular septal defects, atrial septal defects, aortic stenosis, deformed tricuspid valves and patent ductus arteriosus. Many other abnormalities also exist.

Arrhythmias and conduction disturbances, which are relatively rare in cats, are caused by irregular contraction of the heart. Tachycardia is a faster than normal heart rate. Its opposite, brachycardia, is a slower than normal heart rate. Heart contractions may be irregular, premature, or late. Symptoms vary considerably. Some cats may show almost no outward signs, whereas others may suffer serious respiratory distress. Some antiarrhythmic medications, if carefully administered, may be used to treat these types of disorders in cats.

Cardiomyopathy is a disease of unknown etiology of the heart muscle. It causes hypertrophy (overgrowth) or dilation of the heart. Using an ultrasound, a veterinarian can distinguish between the three types—hypertrophic, dilated, restrictive—of cardiomyopathy by analyzing the changes to the heart muscle and cavities. Similar heart lesions are seen in primary myocardial diseases and other disorders such as taurine deficiency and hyperthyroid. The different types of cardiomyopathy have similar symptoms. General symptoms include appetite loss, weakness, and sometimes vomiting. Symptoms more specific to cardiomyopathy are those related to left-sided heart failure (labored breathing, wheezing, and cough) or right-sided heart failure (shortness of breath and ascites—accumulation of serous fluid within the abdominal cavity). A cat having difficulty breathing will present exaggerated breathing movements, sometimes assuming the characteristic crouch with front legs

tucked in close to the chest, and breathing through the mouth. If a clot detaches, the cat may suffer an iliac thromboembolism.

In cases where the cause of the cardiomyopathy is known (hyperthyroid, taurine deficiency), the underlying illness is treated. Cardiomyopathies of unknown origin are treated with various classes of medications, including diuretics, vasodilators, more specifically conversion enzyme inhibitors, and sometimes digitalis-like drugs. Rest, stress management, and a reduced-salt diet are also important to treatment.

Hyperthyroidism is a disorder that occurs in older cats. In the long-term, it leads to heart abnormalities, with symptoms including tachycardia (rapid heart rate) with strong contractions of the heart muscle, and sometimes the appearance of a murmur. As the disease progress, arrhythmia and hypertrophic cardiomyopathy may develop. If a cat is not treated early enough, the illness may be irreversible and result in death. Other clinical signs include weight loss, ravenous appetite, hyperactivity or nervousness, sometimes vomiting, excessive drinking and urinating, and hairloss. A blood test analyzing thyroid hormone levels provides a definitive diagnosis. Hyperthyroidism can be treated with medications (antithyroid drugs) or, more commonly, surgically.

The thyroid is not the only endocrine gland susceptible to disease. The pituitary and adrenal glands may also fail or harbor tumors.

Diabetes mellitus is rare in cats, though is probably under-diagnosed. The initial clinical signs are nonspecific, the most common being excessive thirst (polydipsia) and urination (polyuria). Appetite generally increases, though sometimes drops off. The cat suffering from diabetes mellitus is weak and vomits occasionally. He is sometimes obese and is generally more than five years old. Other diseases or endocrine disorders, such as reproductive or urinary infections, may accompany diabetes mellitus. Blood and/or urine tests confirm the diagnosis.

Glycemia (blood sugar level) is controlled by two opposing hormones—insulin and glucagon—secreted by the pancreas. In 80% of all diabetic cats, insufficient insulin is secreted, while the other 20% secrete sufficient insulin, but their body utilizes it poorly.

Treatment of diabetes mellitus must include a dietary element. Food must have a higher fiber content (green vegetables) and contain complex carbohydrates. If a cat is obese, a lower-calorie diet is required in order to achieve gradual weight loss. A veterinarian can suggest an appropriate food to meet the diabetic cat's dietary requirements.

If appropriate, a veterinarian will also prescribe oral hypoglycemic drugs or insulin therapy. It is difficult to determine the appropriate quantity and dose frequency in cats, as requirements may vary over time. Some cats are only temporary diabetic. Diabetic cats must be seen by a veterinarian regularly and closely monitored.

Diabetes Mellitus and Diabetes Insipidus

Though both diseases bear the same first name, the two should not be confused. Diabetes mellitus is a disease characterized by elevated blood sugar levels (hyperglycemia). Diabetes insipidus is a rare disease caused by the kidney's inability to concentrate urine as a result of deficient pituitary secretion of vasopressin (antidiuretic hormone), which controls urine concentration, or the kidney's inability to respond to the vasopressin hormone.

Most of the body's waste is eliminated by the liver and the kidneys, but these organs can fail.

The functions of the **liver** include the manufacture of certain hormones and bile containing bile salts. The liver is also important in the absorption of fats and detoxification, and plays a vital role in the metabolism of sugars (storage and redistribution), as well as the synthesis of certain proteins and fats. The liver stores vita-

mins A, D, and B12 and mineral salts, including iron and copper. It eliminates toxic products after assailing them with an array of complex chemical reactions. One of the classic detoxification pathways is almost nonexistent in cats. For this reason, cats are extremely sensitive to a variety of products, including insecticides such as DDT and lindane, aspirin, and acetaminophen.

Once the liver ceases functioning, the condition is referred to as liver failure.

Acute liver failure can be attributed to several causes, including infection—FIP, pseudotuberculosis, various bacteria, and toxoplasma—toxins, shock, hemolysis, or immune disorders. Symptoms of liver failure are weakness, inappetence, vomiting, diarrhea, and excessive thirst. Jaundice develops rapidly, and nervous disorders set in—unsteady gait, prostration, followed by coma, and sometimes convulsions. Blood tests can be helpful in making a definitive diagnosis. A veterinarian will treat the cause of the disease if it can be identified and will administer medications to treat the symptoms. Rest and a high-carbohydrate, low-fat, low-protein diet are vital.

The **onset of chronic liver failure** is so subtle that by the time symptoms raise concern, a large portion of the liver has already been destroyed. At this stage, it is almost impossible to determine the cause of the problem.

Possible causes include cholangiohepatitis (inflammation of the biliary tract), infectious diseases such as FIP, endocrine disorders such as diabetes mellitus, as well as cirrhosis of the liver. Cancers of the liver (lymphosarcomas, primary or metastasized carcinomas) produce similar clinical signs.

A cat suffering from liver failure experiences weight loss, has a dull coat, has a reasonable appetite but experiences digestive problems including diarrhea or constipation, and often consumes greater quantities of water than normal. Over time, slight, then more severe jaundice sets in. Blood tests may reveal slight abnormalities.

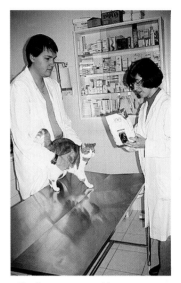

aCat being examined by a veterinarian

A special diet regime is the primary treatment method. A diet rich in high-quality proteins and easily digestible carbohydrates should be fed in several small meals per day.

The **kidneys** may be affected by several disorders.

Acute renal failure corresponds to a significant, sudden decrease or total shutdown of kidney functions. The origin of the failure can be broken down into three categories.

1. Pre-renal, such as hemorrhagic shock, digestive disorders, burns, or heart failure;
2. Renal, including acute nephritis, infection, or toxins;
3. Post-renal, such as obstruction of the urinary tract, whether as the result of inflammation, a tumor, or formation of calculi (stones).

A cat suffering from acute renal failure does not urinate, is depressed and weak, and vomits. Blood and/or urine tests confirm diagnosis. Treatment sometimes requires hospitalization, since the patient must be closely monitored and normally requires an IV.

Chronic renal failure is probably the number one non-accidental cause of death in geriatric cats. As the kidney ages, its ability to cleanse the blood diminishes and toxic wastes begin to accumulate in the blood. The cat loses weight, loses interest in food, vomits, suffers from diarrhea and halitosis (urine smell), and eventually presents nervous disorders (coma) resulting in death. Changing the diet early on by restricting phosphorus increases the life expectancy of a cherished companion. Medical treatment is normally provided at times of crisis or when the condition worsens suddenly. A veterinarian will typically prescribe a special diet, since the onset of chronic renal failure can be delayed through appropriate diet.

Urinary tract obstruction is often the cause of acute renal failure. Cats are plagued by lower urinary tract disorders, all grouped under the heading Feline Urologic Syndrome (FUS). The anatomy of male cats makes them particularly vulnerable.

Dry foods (kibble) have often been blamed for this disorder. In the 1970s, some low quality, high-magnesium foods were responsible for creating alkaline urine, which contributed to the formation of crystals and the accumulation of struvites (magnesium ammonium phosphate calculi). These irritating grains caused cystitis in both genders, obstructing the long, narrow, curved urethra of male cats.

Today, veterinarians have a broader view of this syndrome, now referred to as Feline Lower Urinary Tract Disease (**FLUTD**). This term includes disorders characterized by a variety of clinical signs, including frequent or painful urination or the presence of blood in the urine (hematuria). Urination outside of the litter box can also be a warning sign.

Urinary bacterial infections (rare), tumors, anatomical malformations, urolithiasis (presence of urinary calculi), and idiopathic cystitis may all cause FLUTD.

The urine of a healthy cat contains varying amounts of crystals (struvites, calcium oxalates, etc.). Urinary sediments are not produced by diet, but diet may make a cat more prone to precipitation of these sediments. Cat foods are now formulated to reduce the risk of precipitation of minerals at each stage of an animal's life. Though dry foods are perfectly adapted to the requirements of a healthy cat, wet food or rehydrated dry food should be fed to cats that have previously been diagnosed with a urinary tract stone in order to increase their water intake.

In more than 60% of all cases, a cat suffers from idiopathic cystitis. This involves periods of remission followed by reappearance of symptoms and is the cause of most toilet accidents in cats. Stress plays a major role in the onset of idiopathic cystitis. Stress may be caused by difficulties in the relationship with the owner, a change in food, environmental problems relating to confinement, overcrowding, the litter box, or any number of reasons known only to the cat.

Sometimes an obstruction in male (neutered or intact) cats may not pass due to the size of the obstruction and the accumulation of protein matter. The cat passes only a little urine, or none at all. As a result, the urine accumulates in the bladder. The cat is prostrate and curled up and exhibits signs of intense pain caused by the distention of the bladder. If the bladder is struck, unskillfully palpated, or intervention comes too late, it may rupture. The waste products contained in the urine are resorbed by the body, leading to uremic toxicity. The only option in these cases is surgery.

We greatly appreciate the beauty and softness of the cat's coat. But dermatoses can mar that beauty.

The number one cause of **feline dermatosis** is parasite infestation, notably **flea** infestation.

The cat is susceptible to other more rare skin parasitoses:
including other forms of mange and lice causing miliary dermatitis and itching, cheyletiellosis producing seborrhea sicca, miliary dermatitis lesions, intense itching, and thick dandruff, which are transmissible to humans. The bright orange chigger larvae settle into the folds of the skin, particularly of the cat's ear, in summer. Ticks and demodex (mites) also occasionally feed on cats.

Ringworm invades the skin and the hair. It is caused by a dermatophyte fungus, typically Microsporum canis. These two conditions are discussed in the section on prevention of dermatoses and external fungi.

Miliary Dermatitis

This disease complex is characterized by a crusty rash and flaky skin that feels like fiber-glass. It is typically caused by an allergic reaction to flea bites, but may also be associated with a number of other feline skin conditions. Miliary dermatitis is not actually a disease, per se, but rather the manner in which a cat's skin reacts to various conditions. It is the most common skin disorder in cats. Apart from flea bites, possible causes include:

• Inhalant allergies, such as hypersensitivity to mites in dust; unlike humans, who develop hayfever, the allergic reaction in cats takes the form of itchiness and a scabby rash;
• Food intolerance or hypersensitivity;
• Bacterial folliculitis: bacteria (commonly staphylococcus) accumulate in the hair follicles and cause infection. This is typically the cause of chin acne;
• All skin parasitoses;
• Allergic reaction to medications;
• Malfunctioning of the immune system;
• Contact dermatitis, etc.

Treatment varies depending on the cause of the condition. Common treatments that normally produce satisfactory results include antihistamines, corticosteroids, essential fatty acids, and possibly megestrol acetate.

Cats suffering from **psychogenic alopecia and neurodermatosis** groom themselves incessantly. They lick, clean, and bite at themselves all day long. Some shy cats, or those that have been scolded for constant grooming, often clean themselves only at nighttime or out of view of the owner. All breeds, including strays, are subject to this condition, but Siamese, Orientals, Burmese, and Abyssinians are particularly prone to the disorder. These are also the breeds that commonly suck and eat wool. Once again, this condition is a disease complex, not a single disease. Many believe that it is purely stress-induced (possible stress factors being the introduction of a new cat into the household, loss of a loved one—animal or human—boredom, etc.). Others hold that it is exclusively an allergic reaction, and that the stress factors simply aggravate the condition.

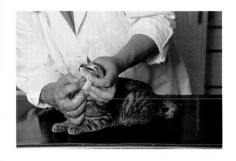

Hormonal causes seem to be rare, though they are often mentioned as a possible explanation. If an underlying cause is uncovered, it is typically (in order of frequency) an allergic reaction to flea bites, an inhalant or food allergy, ringworm, or parasites.

The primary symptom of a **food allergy** is intense itching. This hypersensitivity to one or more elements in food can develop at any age. It is difficult to identify the particular offending substance(s), but without identifying the specific cause, the condition will not improve. In addition to constant itching, a cat suffering from a food allergy may also present milliary dermatitis, scabs on the head and neck, and thickened, irritated patches of skin.

Eosinophilic granuloma complex is a group of skin disorders specific to cats. It produces lesions that develop and spread gradually. Examination of the lesions reveals an abundance of eosinophilic cells.

Eosinophilic granuloma complex can be divided into three different categories. The eosinophilic ulcer, or indolent ulcer, almost always occurs on the upper lip. The eosinophilic plaque is an oozing, often ulcerated, lesion that causes intense itching. It typically occurs on the abdomen and inner thighs. Eosinophilic granuloma lesions appear in relatively straight lines and are firm areas of hair loss, most commonly occurring on the backs of the hindlimbs. The condition may clear up spontaneously in young cats, but older cats typically experience relapses and worsening of the condition. Some medications, including corticosteroids, offer some improvement of the lesions, but a definitive cure is elusive.

A cat's **eyes**, which lend charm and personality, are also subject to several diseases.

Congenital **eyelid disorders** may include the absence of an upper eyelid or entropion—inward turning of the eyelid causing the eyelashes to scratch the cornea and creating lesions. Surgery is required to correct these conditions. Blepharitis, infection of the eyelids, is caused by bacteria or fungi (ringworm).

The eyes are lubricated by **tears**. Insufficient tear production can lead to serious eye conditions, such as keratoconjunctivitis sicca.
Tears drain from the eyes through narrow lacrimal canaliculi (ducts), which sometimes become plugged as the result of infection or a congenital deformity. If tears do not drain properly, they flow down the sides of the nose leaving brownish markings.

Conjunctival diseases are common in cats. They are often one of the symptoms of a more general disease and are one of the early symptoms of chlamydiosis. The herpesvirus of infectious rhinotracheitis is responsible for a mucuslike, pussy discharge as well as keratitis punctata or serious corneal ulcerations, either during the acute stage of the illness or as a chronic condition following the primary infection.

Cat's sometimes develop **corneal lesions** that are unique to the feline species, such as corneal sequestrum, characterized by the formation of a blackish plaque on the corneal surface.

Uveitis causes the coloration of the iris to change. The iris becomes dull and pinkish, and the surface becomes hazy and rough. There are three types of uveitis specific to cats. They are part of the clinical presentation of feline leukemia, feline immunodeficiency virus, and feline infectious peritonitis. Uveitis may also appear in cases of toxoplasmosis, trauma, or eye infections.

Glaucoma, an elevation of intraocular pressure beyond normal levels, increases the volume of the eye and causes extreme pain.
The integrity of the **retina** is essential to good vision. Hemorrhages within the retina and retinal detachment may appear following trauma or serious illness. These two conditions are

also complications of uveitis. Retinal degeneration caused by taurine deficiency is no longer an issue, since commercial foods now contain adequate quantities of this essential amino acid. Dog food does not contain sufficient quantities of taurine, therefore it is not appropriate to feed cats dog food.

Finally, cats may also suffer from four **nervous disorders affecting the eyes**: Strabismus, third eyelid prolapse, Horner's syndrome (contraction of the pupil in one eye and prolapse of the third eyelid), dilated pupil syndrome, and feline dysautonomia.

Prolapse of the third eyelid

The cat has a third eyelid located at the inner corner of the eye. It helps protect the eye and distribute tears to protect the cornea. Sometimes, this third eyelid remains continuously visible for a variety of reasons:

• Mechanical causes related to the condition of the eye - microphthalmos (abnormally small eye) or atrophy of the eyeball, extreme weight loss, tumors, or trauma to retractor muscles caused by a scratch.

• Neurological causes irritating the area or disrupting equilibrium, an overactive parasympathetic system, or following an abdominal condition.

• Lesion of the cervical sympathetic nerves caused by a variety of conditions, including a herniated disc, otitis, a tumor, an abscess, or trauma.

In cats, most cases of prolapsed third eyelid follow an abdominal disorder. This is why the veterinarian is particularly interested in the health of the cat's digestive tract and often prescribes a laxative (for hairballs), a dewormer (undetected *dipylidium* tapeworm infections often produce this type of symptoms), or an intestinal antiseptic.

As the life expectancy of cats has increased, the number of **cancers** diagnosed has also risen. Perhaps cats, like us, are also suffering from the problems, such as pollution or an owner who smokes, associated with modern society.

A tumor—uncontrolled proliferation of cells—may be benign or malignant. A malignant tumor is called cancer. In cats, malignant tumors are six times more common than benign tumors after the age of three. Skin cancer is the most common cancer in the cat population as a whole, followed by mammary tumors, then various cancers of the soft tissues.

The occurrence of glandular tumors and lymphosarcomas is directly related to the feline leukemia infection rate.

Symptoms of cancer vary depending on the organ affected, the rate of growth of the tumor, whether it is localized or has metastasized, and its impact on other parts of the body (for example, a tumor in the endocrine gland).

Nevertheless, there are some general warning signs that warrant a trip to the veterinarian. Cancer produces localized and non-localized effects. Localized effects include a lump or visible or palpable swelling, destruction of the organ, compression of nearby organs or impaired function. Non-localized effects result from excessive or absence of production of a hormone, or production of substances by the tumor itself. Several non-specific signs may indicate cancer and merit further exploration.

These include weight loss, increased thirst or appetite, convulsions, cough, and internal or external bleeding.

If a veterinarian suspects a cancerous tumor, she will typically perform additional tests to confirm her diagnosis or to provide a more precise diagnosis. Some tests for tumors include x-rays, ultrasounds, and other more expensive techniques such as MRI or scanning. Yet another technique involves examining biopsied tissue or effused liquid under a microscope.

In animals, surgery is the primary treatment for cancerous tumors. Chemotherapy is sometimes elected in conjunction with surgery, or as the sole treatment method. Radiation therapy, in conjunction with surgery and/or chemotherapy, and immunotherapy are promising new techniques, but are still in the development stages.

Study of cancer in cats is of interest to comparative pathology. Feline leukemia, caused by infection with the feline leukemia virus, is one of the oldest known diseases for which researchers have been able to demonstrate cause and effect between a viral infection and the development of tumors.

The tumors most commonly associated with feline leukemia are lymphosarcomas. Though FIV (feline immunodeficiency virus) is not recognized as an oncogenic (causing tumor formation) disease, cats infected with FIV have a higher incidence of certain cancers, such as lymphosarcomas, myeloid tumors, and sarcomas.

Ear cancer in white cats

White-eared cats frequently exposed to the sun run a much greater risk of developing a cancerous tumor. Chronic irritation from the sun's rays gradually evolves, eventually resulting in squamous cell carcinoma. This type of tumor generally affects white-eared cats over eight years of age. The cancer first affects only the edge of the ear, then quickly spreads to the surrounding tissues. To protect your white-eared cat against cancer of the ears, keep him indoors in summer and during peak sunlight hours. Before the cancer spreads to the entire earflap, the edges of the ears should be amputated. Owners should be aware that recurrence is not uncommon despite amputation.

Diseases of Older Cats

The life expectancy of cats, at least those that receive medical care and loving attention, is increasing. It is important to recognize the disorders that can affect older cats so that they can be treated effectively.

• Coat and claws: The coat sometimes becomes so matted, particularly on the back and lumbar region, that thick knots form which cannot be brushed out. The claws also need special care since the older cat is not as active as he once was. Older cats require daily brushing and combing, and claws should be trimmed regularly. The older cat will appreciate this loving attention, which will stimulate his own desire to groom and improve his overall state of mind, warding off depression.

• Eyes: The color of the iris changes as a cat ages, and the pupil becomes opaque. This sclerosis of the lens, physiological in origin, has very little effect on eyesight.

• Teeth: Some cats have tartar buildup and begin losing teeth at a relatively young age. Oral hygiene products are available to keep the teeth clean, and a veterinarian can remove tartar buildup, or extract teeth if necessary.

• Sensory organs: The senses tend to diminish with age.

• Heart: Heart failure is rare, except in cases of hyperthyroidism.

• Endocrine glands: These glands are often affected by the aging process. Diabetes is not uncommon and is difficult to control.

• Digestive System: With age, a cat's digestive enzymes become less efficient, and as a result, older cats tend to lose weight. Chronic diarrhea is sometimes a problem.

• Reproduction: Reproduction declines gradually with age. Most mammary tumors are malignant, and therefore prognosis is generally not promising.

- Respiratory system: The health of the respiratory systems depends more on the medical history of the individual cat than age.

- Musculoskeletal system: Unfortunately, arthritis and joint pain is the lot of the older cat.

- Kidneys: Owners should be on the lookout for symptoms of chronic kidney failure.

- Cancer and tumors: The occurrence of cancer increases with age.

Household Dangers

Though indoor/outdoor cats are more likely to contract infectious diseases and fall victim to an accident, indoor cats are not entirely out of harms way. Cats of all ages fall, but young cats run the greatest risk of falling, since they are still exploring the limits of their environment. Therefore, it is wise to place a screen or net around terraces and balconies.

The kitchen is filled with many potential dangers—hot burners, boiling water, hot food, fryers, knives, open bottles, strings tied around meat, etc.

An iron is also a potential hazard, as are electrical cords. Young cats love to chew. If they bite through an electrical cord, they may suffer a severe burn on the mouth in the best case scenario, and death by electrocution in the worst case scenario.

Cats can drown in washing machines, bathtubs, or even in the toilet bowl.

Cats are rarely poisoned by household products because they are finicky about what they eat, but many houseplants cause irritation or are poisonous to cats.

Some toys, such as bells and strings, also pose a threat. Never leave a threaded needle lying around.

The Most Common Types of Poisoning

Cats tend to taste their food before indulging, so poisoning is fairly uncommon. However, some poisons have a taste that the cat likes, or a cat may eat small prey that has consumed toxic products.

Cats lack detoxification mechanisms and are less likely than dogs to regurgitate disagreeable substances. A cat's nervous system is very easily disrupted by a number of poisons.

SHOULD I ALTER MY CAT?

If a vet is asked to sterilize a cat, he will probably suggest removal of the sex glands—castration for males and ovariectomy for females.

Age at castration is unimportant. However, the longer an owner waits to have a male cat neutered, the more established undesirable sexual behaviors, such as marking and roaming, become. A reasonable age seems to be somewhere between six and eight months of age. Castration (removal of the testicles) is the only method that renders a cat infertile and represses sex drive. A vasectomy, cutting of the vas deferens through which sperm are transported, renders a cat infertile, but in no way alters sexual behaviors.

It is a good idea to spay female cats as soon as possible after the onset of puberty, preferably when the cat is not in heat. If a female cat has managed to mate and becomes pregnant before the owner was able to have her neutered, an overiectomy can still be performed once she is no longer in heat. The procedure ends the pregnancy. Sometimes, a veterinarian prefers to perform an ovariohysterectomy, in which the ovaries and the uterus are removed. This procedure is commonly elected if lesions caused by hyperplasia, cysts, infection, or pregnancy, for example, are found on the uterus during surgery.

If an owner wishes to wait until the female cat is older, medical contraception is a viable temporary solution.

Dangerous products include:
- • Pesticides
- agricultural herbicides
- chlorinated hydrocarbons used to treat wood (sawdust from treated wood should not be used for litter)
- carbamate insecticides
- chloralose, the chemical used to kill rodents and crows. Sadly individuals who have no respect for the law or animals also use this product to kill cats.
- strychnine and crimidine, the two most common convulsants
- metaldehyde, used in gardens to control snails and slugs
- anticoagulants, most commonly ingested by eating a poisoned rodent.

- • Medications
- external parasite medications, most often resulting from incorrect application

- aspirin (aspirin is sometimes used for iliac thromboses, but should only be administered in small doses and strictly under the supervision of a veterinarian)
- acetaminophen.

• Plants: Young cats are the most commonly affected after playing with the leaves of plants, particularly houseplants, such as Dieffenbachia.

• Pollutants and various household chemical products, such as white spirits and antifreeze.

Though the conditions described in this chapter are the most common, they by no means represent an exhaustive list of the afflictions that can befall cats. If in doubt, consult your veterinarian immediately. In most cases, early treatment greatly increases the likelihood of complete recovery, ensuring that you and your cat will enjoy a long life together.

THE CAT AND THE LAW

As cat populations grow, countries around the world are creating new laws to regulate cats' place in society.

In general, most countries regulate the legal status, sale, trade, breeding, mandatory registration, insurance, identification, vaccination, and protection of the animal and its environment, and have laws in place with regard to owners responsibilities vis-à-vis society.

For information regarding a specific country, contact the local feline association for that country (see Useful Addresses on p. 448).

The veterinarian and your cat

Though there are more cats in France than dogs, cats are seen less often at veterinary offices than dogs. So why are owners more likely to take their dog to the vet?

Generally, cat owners avoid taking their cat to the vet because they are afraid the trip will not go well. Cats tend to get very upset about visits to the vet. They do not like to leave home, and certainly have no interest in a clinic filled with the smells of other cats. And being independent creatures, they do not appreciate being required to stand immobile on the examination table, to be poked and prodded by a stranger and worse yet, stuck with needles.

The owner's presence during an examination will help calm the cat.

Urban owners tend also to think that their indoor cats are safe from infectious diseases, whereas owners living in rural areas do not feel the need to invest in vaccinations and sterilization, arguing that their cats will probably die young anyway as the result of an accident, possibly being struck by a car or shot by a careless neighbor.

The cat himself is also partly at fault. Cats rarely complain and adapt readily to their handicaps. They often hide their illness well, so owners do not become concerned until the symptoms are very serious. Anemia commonly goes unnoticed for an extended period of time. The cat suffering from anemia is often not taken to see a veterinarian until the terminal stage of the illness, when hemoglobin levels are low and the red blood cell count has plummeted. In anemia, the blood is no longer able to carry sufficient quantities of oxygen, so the cat becomes winded easily. But he adapts by limiting his activity. It is not until the disease is very advanced, when hemoglobin levels are down to 4 or 5 g/dl (normal levels being 10 to 15 g/dl), that the owner finally notices that something is wrong.

Despite all this, cats receive considerably more attention from their owners and veterinarians now than they did in the past. Some basic practices will help your cat "survive" a trip to the vet.

Transporting a cat

Your cat will feel much more secure if he is transported in a cat carrier. Make sure he is in the carrier when you take him out to the car and when he is in the waiting room. (Note that some cats prefer to move about freely in the car, rather than remain in their carrier.) The carrier serves as a hiding place, protecting the cat from humans and other animals, dogs and cats alike. The carrier also provides protection against disease, shielding your cat from the secretions of a sneezing cat suffering from rhinitis. If you take a taxi rather than your own car, chose a watertight plastic carrier that will not allow urine or vomit to escape from the bottom if your cat has an accident. If your cat refuses to get into the carrier, turn him around and put him in backend first. If your cat tends to be aggressive toward the veterinarian, select a carrier that opens from the top (basket type). The vet will have less difficult taking hold of the cat. If instead, you make the trip to the veterinarian on foot, chose a soft carrier with a flat bottom, which is easier to carry. Some very calm cats will walk on a leash and others like to ride on their owner's shoulder, though many become agitated when they arrive in the waiting room since they have nowhere to hide.

The visit

Most veterinarians prefer that the owner remain in the room with the cat to offer reas-

surance. It is important that the cat be able to see or smell his owner at all times. Timid cats like to hide their head under their owner's arm or a piece of clothing.

A cat is generally only minimally restrained during examination. The veterinarian holds the cat on the examination table with one hand placed on the front of the chest. If an injection or painful palpation is required, the veterinarian will hold the cat by the scruff of the neck so that he cannot escape. Though this may look uncomfortable, it causes no pain to the animal.

Taking blood or capturing a urine sample may require a veterinary assistant and firmer restraint. The owner must make an effort to remain calm since cats are very sensitive to the moods of their owners. Speed and composure are the keys to success, so the cat does not become impatient or panic.

In rare instances, a veterinarian will be required to take more extreme measures to restrain a particularly aggressive cat. Sometimes a cat becomes so upset that he panics and loses control, turning into a whirling dervish biting and scratching at everything within reach, even his owner, whom he no longer recognizes. In such situations, thick gloves and a large towel are called for to restrain the cat. Though this method may seem cruel upon first consideration, it is actually in the best interest of all concerned, since it prevents the cat from injuring himself and others.

Symptoms

It is difficult to treat cats because their symptoms are often well hidden, and the same symptoms—inappetence, vomiting, reclusion—are common to several diseases. Unlike dogs, which complain when they are in pain, cats simply stop all activity, conserve energy, and hide. Fortunately for veterinarians, owners often notice minor behavioral changes. Therefore, before the veterinarian examines the animal, it is important that the owner describe in detail everything out of the ordinary that he has noticed. This discussion time will also give the cat a chance to relax a bit and feel more at ease.

The clinical examitation

Next, the veterinarian will examine the cat. This important step must be done in such a way that it does not overly stress the animal. The veterinarian will inspect the color of the mucous membranes, smell the cat's breath, and examine the coat. She will use an ophthalmoscope to examine the eyes and an otoscope for the ears. Next, she will palpate the abdomen, which is typically fairly easy since a

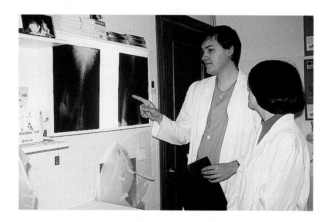

cat is quite small. When palpating, the vet is looking for abnormal masses, such as swollen glands, tumors, or foreign bodies. At the same time, she checks the consistency of the bladder and the intestines. Finally, using a stethoscope, the veterinarian will listen to the cat's lungs and heart. Cats have a rapid heart rate, beating 200 times per minute on average, but reaching as much as 260 beats per minutes when the cat is frightened. It can be difficult to hear the lungs and heart clearly if the cat is purring, often the case with kittens and extremely sick geriatric cats. In geriatric cats, this purring is not a sign of pleasure, but instead a sign that the cat is suffering.

Additional tests, such as blood and/or urine analysis, x-rays, ultrasound, or biopsy, are often necessary to make a definitive diagnosis. Since cats show few outward signs, a veterinarian

must apply all her knowledge and insight to diagnose the cat's specific condition.

Fortunately, feline medicine is growing by leaps and bounds, due in large part to demand on the part of cat owners who are increasingly concerned about the health and well-being of their small companions. Cats that visit the veterinarian regularly, beginning at a very young age for vaccinations, become accustomed to being handled.

Feline medicine in France and abroad

Feline medicine has made remarkable advances since the 1960s. It is the field of internal medicine that has developed the most, starting with the identification of viral diseases, then the leukemia virus, immunodeficiency syndrome, and feline infectious peritonitis, followed by urinary tract disorders (such as kidney failure and cystitis, leading to the development of new "urinary tract health" foods), liver disorders (the various forms of hepatitis responsible for jaundice), and most recently, heart disorders which are now easier to identify thanks to advances in ultrasound and Doppler technologies.

The English-speaking world is particularly advanced in this field. Cornell University in New York formed a department devoted exclusively to feline medicine twenty-five years ago. The University of Bristol in the United Kingdom led the way in Europe, creating a feline medicine department in 1993. In France, breeders and veterinarians have formed the Société française de félinotechnie (S.F.F.), which organizes conferences focusing exclusively on cat health issues.

Cat clinics

Veterinary clinics devoted exclusively to cats have appeared in some countries, springing from a passion for cats. The first cat clinic was founded by Dr. Barbara Stein in Chicago in

1975. Many others followed suit, and now more than three hundred cat clinics exist in the United States alone. The first cat clinic in Europe opened in Denmark in October 1987. Similar clinics opened soon after in Great Britain and France. Access to these clinics is reserved exclusively to cats, in order to avoid introducing the smells and noises of other animals, which could disturb the cats.

The field of cat medicine is progressing at a swift pace. Cat owners, breeders, researchers, and veterinarians alike have taken notice. These cat lovers are delighted with all the attention that the object of their affections is receiving!

Hospitalization

When a cat is hospitalized, certain steps are taken to make the cat as comfortable as possible. Cats scare easily and require considerable sleep—18 hours per day on average. Cats are housed away from barking dogs, since if a cat cannot sleep, it becomes irritable. Moreover, cats love comfort, so they should not be placed in a cold, empty cage. A bed and cushion must be provided, and a piece of clothing with familiar smells, such as the owners scarf or sweater, will be a comfort. The area must be heated. Though cats do not like noise, they do enjoy some level of activity, such as watching birds outside a window or the presence or movement of people. This allows the cat to enjoy his favorite activity—watching the world go by as he relaxes. Cats enjoy a visit by their owner, and it is often during such visits that cats begin eating again after undergoing surgery. The visit also gives the cat incentive to get his legs back under him so he can walk over to see his owner. Cats like to keep clean, therefore every attempt should be made to groom them—brushing, cleaning the eyes and the mouth, etc. It's the little things that count. Grooming, petting, the cat's favorite food, sweet talk... all help keep a cat's spirits up. When outside his familiar environment, a cat can easily give up hope, no matter how good the medical attention that he receives.

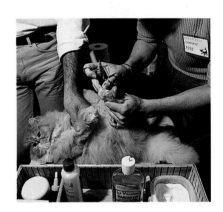

SYMPTOMS THAT WARRANT A VISIT TO THE VET

- Coughing or sneezing
- Runny eyes and/or nose
- Drooling, the cat stops grooming himself (gingivitis and toothache)
- Recurring vomiting and diarrhea
- Labored breathing with exaggerated chest motion (presence of liquid in the chest)
- Yellow skin and mucous membranes: Gums, conjunctiva, earflap (sign of jaundice)
- Any mass or growth on or under the skin or near the mammary glands (possible tumor)
- Vaginal discharge: Pus or blood (sign of metritis or uterine cancer)
- Increased water intake coupled with excessive urination (sign of liver or kidney failure or diabetes)
- The cat crouches by the water bowl, but does not drink
- The cat has "accidents" (urinates or defecates outside of the litter box)
- Frequent trips to the litter box, but the cat is unable to urinate or produces only a few drops of urine (cystitis)
- The cat suddenly becomes aggressive and begins biting (possible toothache)
- A geriatric cat that suddenly begins running into furniture (vision loss caused by hypertension)

Coordination Royal Canin: Catherine Legros
Project Editors: Diffomédia / Paris
Art Director: Guy Rolland
Coordination: Béatrice Fortamps,
assisted by: Céline Davaze and Valérie de Leval
Illustrations: Agnès Pezon
Cover: Somali - © Hermeline/Cogis

© 2003 Aniwa SA
Publisher: Aniwa Publishing
10, rue du Colisée - F.-75008 - Paris
Tel.: + 33 (0)1 44 95 02 20/Fax: + 33 (0)1 44 95 02 22
www.aniwa.com
Copyright: first quarter 2003
Printed in CEE